Hi WYATT !

MERRY CHRISTMAS...

GREAT GRANDPARENTS

YOU HAVE...

DECMEBER 2013

Dave & Barbara Hubert

Christmas Major
The Fire Horse Who Saved Christmas

Dave Hubert

Barbara Hubert

Edited by Judy R. Craig

Produced and published by:
DEER VALLEY PRESS
5125 Deer Valley Road
Rescue, California 95672
(530) 676-7401
www.deervalleypress.com

Library of Congress Control Number: 2013937285
ISBN 978-1-931301-28-2

First printed in August 2013
Printed in China

Table of Contents

Acknowledgements

My father, "Spike," had a great statement: "You know how rich you are by the number of friends who care for you." Well, I guess I am truly rich, for not only do I have friends I can count on, but also a family that has always been there. So, with honor and heartfelt thanks, Barbara and I acknowledge our family and friends! The only thing wrong is that we would need another ten pages to truly list all of them!

Top of the list, we want to thank our son, Mark, and daughter, Michelle, who have exceeded all of our expectations and are always there for us. God has truly blessed us with great kids.

To our long list of friends: Thanks for being there, and helping us with life. Specific thanks goes to:

- Our remarkable publisher, Bill Teie, of Deer Valley Press, for his never-ending guidance, gifted layout abilities, and attention to detail to ensure the book is the best it can be, plus all the general help Bill has given us with absolutely everything throughout the entire, extensive book-writing process.

- Judy Craig, our book editor, for her contagious enthusiasm, skilled understanding of English, and extremely creative way with words.

- Jimmy and Betty Glynn, friends and owners of the real Major, our very first, true fire horse who pulled our steamer in many events over the years.

- Our great horse professionals, George and Buddy Liblin from G and F Carriages, for their years of loyal service pulling our steam fire engine with their magnificent teams of horses, and for giving equestrian advice to ensure the book history regarding the draft horses was accurate.

- Steve Morse, Phil Yuhas, and Michelle Ramirez for their valuable review(s) and significant input during the early drafts of the story.

- Our learned fire historians, Ray and Judi Russell, for their continued assistance throughout the book.

- The Fire Service . . . what a profession to be part of. What a wonderful way to help and support the community at large, from medical responses right down to protecting the homes where we all live. Speaking for myself, it has been all I ever wanted from a profession: respectable, exciting, honorable, surprising, technical, real, always challenging, and at times, somewhat hilarious. A big "fire family" that is outside the little personal family, but just as close and meaningful as one could ask for. It is so reassuring to know our firefighters are always there to help when we call them.

- The real Blaze, our priceless Dalmatian, who has accompanied us on hundreds of Steamer events for over fifteen years—performing fire-prevention education tricks for little children, and patiently visiting with them for hours on end during events. Because of our devotion to Blaze, she is portrayed as Christmas Major's lifelong friend in the book.

- And finally, to horses and dogs everywhere! A nudge from a big horse's head, a slobbery kiss from a dog—both are gifts to be proud of—if you're lucky enough to get them. Our animals give us companionship, unquestioning love, and unending devotion. Certainly something worthy of acknowledgement.

Gratefully,

Dave Hubert   Barbara Hubert

Foreword

Starting with the **California Division of Forestry** (CDF) and later becoming Assistant Chief of the California State Fire Training Program in the state Fire Marshal's Office, I was a member of the Fire Service for fifty years and nine months. During my career, I had many great experiences, both good and bad, as any member of the Fire Service will likely also tell you.

Ray M. Russell

I was eventually transferred to the CDF contract in Orange County, California. My first assignment was Captain at Fire Station 22 in Laguna Hills. While assigned there, we placed in service the first ladder truck used in the CDF. That gave us a crew of nine firefighters. One of them was Dave Hubert. It was evident to me that Dave was going to be a lifelong, dedicated member of the Fire Service. One of the first things I recognized was Dave's talent for doing sketches and artwork. Most of his art was fire service-oriented. You will see Dave's artistic talent featured as illustrations for this book.

During my time in the Fire Service, my friend, Ronny J. Coleman and I developed a fire helmet, and sold over 350,000 helmets through Phenix Technology to various fire agencies all over the world. We also started the Phenix Fire Museum, which now has some 3,000-plus items dating back to 1740, and from all over the world. We have several pieces of Dave Hubert's art on display in our museum.

Dave was always ready to help when we needed artwork for our company or our museum. Our leather helmet filigree was designed by him, including our 9-11 Presentation Helmet.

Let me tell you about this book you will be reading. After I read *"Christmas Major,"* I felt that—along with his great art ability—Dave is also a very talented writer. I hope he writes many more!

The Fire Service in the United States has a colorful and exciting history. The first organized firefighting efforts were documented in the time of the colonies, and were carried out with buckets of water. In 1654, the first hand pumper was put into service. It was pulled to the fire by men. Hand pump fire engines were used for the next 125 years as the main method of fire protection in America.

As cities grew and buildings became larger, hand pumps became inadequate for firefighting. Those battles required larger volumes of water, larger hook-and-ladder wagons, and hose wagons. Around 1854, with the advent of steam-powered fire pumpers, it was almost impossible for men to quickly pull the heavy apparatus to a fire. The horse was the answer, thus igniting a romance with the fire horse. Horses became members of fire house families, and were cared for and cherished by the firemen. Fire horses were critical to firefighting until they began to be replaced in the 1920s when motorized fire apparatus started to take hold in American fire departments.

"Christmas Major" is a story about a young fireman named Nicklaus Hollyday who was orphaned at birth. You will travel with him through the hardships he endured as a youth, his quest to become a fireman, marry and start a family—and you will feel inspired by the love and devotion he gave to a horse named Major. You will see how Nick found Major, and trained him from a colt to become a proud, dedicated, and legendary fire horse!

How did this fire horse get the name Christmas Major? That's a question that this book will answer. *"Christmas Major"* is an incredibly entertaining book that I wasn't able to put down until I was finished! I would like to congratulate Dave and Barbara for an outstanding job in developing this book, and I thank you both for allowing me the pleasure of reading it.

Ray M. Russell

Ray M. Russell

*RETIRED MEMBER OF THE FIRE SERVICE
AND FIRE SERVICE HISTORIAN*

Introduction

Well, here I am in my early seventies, and most thankful for my life and all that has happened to me. I have the perfect wife, good health, great kids and grandkids, two real fire dogs, and forty years well spent as a professional fireman. Starting as a rookie in a young county fire department with twelve fire stations—and retiring from that same great department that now has grown to over seventy-four fire stations—I truly have seen it all during my life of high exposure (both good and bad) in public service!

Wanting to stay active in retirement, my son and I restored a 1902 horse-drawn steam fire engine that was in dire need of repair. During the five years of bringing this great machine back to life, I studied much of the history of

horse-drawn fire equipment, as well as the various horse teams and fire dogs that accompanied that rich and exciting time in our country. Today we call her *"The American"* due to the fact she was built by the American Fire Engine Company; the great-grandfather of the American La France Fire Engines.

The day the steamer arrived!

Many parts of this fictional story are true, based on my experiences. As a young child in Connecticut, I remember my dad taking me to the Hartford Fire Department (which I re-named "Markford" in this story after my son, Mark, who is also a firefighter). After visiting the headquarters' fire station and hearing stories of the dedicated firemen and fire horses, I can truly say I was sold on the fire service at a very early age.

The Hartford Orphanage building also had a special meaning to me. My dad would always threaten to *"take me to the orphanage and drop me off"* if I didn't behave! I still remember the looming image of that cold, brick orphanage down from the fire department on a winter day, somewhere around 1945, way back then. I thought my father was serious about the orphanage; today I still wonder . . . .

He was a good, big, strong man who could fix anything. He formed my life, and just like the capable maintenance man from the story, his nickname was also, "Spike."

Once the steamer restoration project was completed, we began using it as part of a public-relations program traveling throughout California in the interest of fire prevention education, thanks to the sponsorship of the California State Firefighters' Association (CSFA). A team of retired firefighters graciously volunteer their time and effort at our events. Little did we all know how meaningful this magnificent project would become, and how deeply it would affect the lives of our families and our friends. Funny how big, colorful, metal things can be so exciting!

The steamer is completed, and about to make its debut at the Rose Parade in 1997. From left to right: Mark, Michelle, Barbara, and Dave, up in the seat.

Another feature in **"Christmas Major"** is the lively fire dog. As a young boy, I remember Chucky, my great black Lab, who was always with me—even in the bathtub! We shared a wonderful twelve years of life together, which taught me how to love things that can't talk, yet can comfort you just with just a look. Today it is Blaze and Dottie, our beloved Dalmatians, who give us joy.

For the past fifteen years, Blaze has been a key part of our Steamer Team program, performing a variety of memorable fire prevention education tricks for children. Blaze has remained a loyal, dedicated member of our team, sitting patiently atop the steamer for hours on end as the curious little children climb up to sit and visit with her.

Blaze

With Blaze close to "retirement" age, we now have a second Dalmatian we named "Dottie" to be her little assistant. Everyone told me, "Dalmatians don't make good pet dogs." But I have since learned—first hand—that all the love and discipline you invest early in pet relationships comes back to you in a rewarding payoff. I truly believe I have the "perfect" dogs and, as the years pass, they continue to give back more love and devotion than I could have ever imagined.

Now, for the real star of the book—Major—who was, for us, an actual, real fire horse.

Major belonged to Jimmy and Betty Glynn, horse people of the highest caliber. Major was a light grey Percheron, 18 hands high, weighing 2,000 pounds, with huge 10-inch hooves.

Dottie

Simply put, Major was "best of the breed." He was stately, mannerly, smart, calm, well-trained, and strong. He always did his very best to please us, and still I tear up thinking about him and all that he did for us, and how good we all looked at our events because of Major. Horse folks have a saying: "his tugs were always tight—" that means he was always pulling more than his share, even if the outside horses weren't. That saying was certainly true about Major.

Sadly, our magnificent Major recently died of old age in a cool, green pasture at his home in central California.

Much of the inspiration for the story came from both my firefighting

Major, Dave, and Blaze in 2002. Note the size of Major's head!

experiences, and what we do today in public relations and fire prevention programs. Major, Blaze, and our restored steam fire engine are the basis of the story.

Of the over 800 events we have participated in over the past sixteen years, one stands out for its richness in feeling and emotion. This specific day, Major played a central and very inspirational role in relieving the suffering of young children, and helping them have a day filled with joy, as it did for us, too.

George Liblin of G&F Carriages and Blaze enjoying the ride during the 2004 Ventura County Fair Parade.

It happened around Christmas time in 1999, when we received a request for a parade appearance. We were also asked to visit a big hospital for terminally ill children in the same town while we were there for the parade.

The day before the hospital visit, we discovered that the tiled patio where the visit was planned was very slippery. So, we had to make some horse "booties" (a kind of padded shoe cover that fits over the hoof) the night before, to ensure the horses would not slip on the smooth, hard surface. After we finished making the covers, late that night in the parking lot I drew the Nike® Logo on the sides of Major's booties—the kind of "inside joke" that we firemen enjoy every now and then!

We brought the big steamer, the new hose wagon, and five draft horses for the event. As we staged the large, colorful trucks, fire wagons, and horses in the hospital's parking lot, we could see the children looking out of their windows and waving at us. It was like the circus had come to town! They seemed so excited with their huge smiles!

Well, on Friday afternoon, everything worked like a charm. We came into the hospital's patio atrium with Jimmy Glynn handling Major. All of us retired firemen were in our old parade uniforms, followed Jimmy and Major, hoping

Major would not perform the particular spectacle of going to the bathroom in the atrium—as he so often did!

The children were already there, sitting in their hospital beds with IVs, monitors, and all sorts of medical instruments

Jimmy Glynn driving his team of Percherons in 1999, Blaze the Dalmation racing alongside, and Dave Hubert riding the steamer tailboard.

connected to them. I will never forget the sound as we walked into the tile-floored atrium. I wish each of you could have heard the *"WOW'S!"* that I did. I wish you all could have seen the little, sad eyes light up as I did, and hear Major's padded hooves hitting the floor, adding to the excitement.

And don't think for a minute that the kids didn't notice the faux Nike® logo! It caused a big laugh for all the children: *"Major had on his Nikes®!"*

Now, I spent thirty years on the front lines of the fire service, and thought I had seen it all—until this day came along. I had never seen a whole group of small children gathered together—in hospital beds—with another common bond: each had a medical diagnosis saying there was no hope of physical recovery.

It was very sad, to say the least.

But, for those few moments, those children looked with wide-eyed smiles at big Major as if to say, *"WOW! Is that horse real?"* Many of the children there had never even seen a horse up so close, let alone one as huge as Major!

It so happened that there were just the same number of children as firemen (six).

We each took a child and talked briefly with them, and we talked about them first: How ya doing? What's your name? We firemen were very happy to be there for them. Then we introduced Major the Fire Horse! Each child had individual time with the big horse, who was the perfect gentleman.

I don't know how—and I won't question why—but it seemed Major knew exactly what was going on. Gentle, quiet, standing straight and head high, I swear I saw him smile. We all marveled as he so gracefully moved around the beds with the children. It was hard to believe he was a giant, 2,000-pound horse.

The child I was talking with had been in the hospital for most of his eight years. He had blond hair, light blue eyes, and a smile as big as our truck's. He told me matter-of-factly that he was going to die soon. I had a difficult time with that. My eyes got watery, and at times it was very hard to talk. (Today, it is still the same.)

Wide-eyed, he looked at Major, and said he had never seen a live horse in person until today. We were last in line to see Major, and as the boy checked out the big animal, petting his nose, he asked me if he could ride Major, *"like a cowboy."*

Without checking with the doctors or nurses, I said, "Sure!"

I gathered some help from the staff—and some from my fellow firemen—and together, we lifted the young boy up on Major's wide back. Firemen on both sides managed the boy's IV and medical apparatus; I held the boy firmly; and Jimmy led Major as the young patient went for the horse ride of a lifetime around that patio.

Then, the boy said he wanted to "drive" Major! Whereupon Jimmy just calmly gave the boy the reins. Because of all his training, Major knew exactly what to do, and did it.

We all worried about what was going to happen next, but we had no reason to, as—true to his character—Major calmly walked around the patio again, with his little blond cowboy in control.

Now, of course, every child wanted a ride! So, we were blessed to be able to give six wonderful rides to six wonderful children on that very fine Friday.

Major gave each of them a special gift that we, alone, never could have. For the precious moments of that Friday afternoon, children who were used to pain and needles—and being tethered to IVs and monitors—were strong, capable, accomplished range riders, easily handling a horse that seemed bigger than life!

The children we visited that day have since been released from their earthly pain, and now our wonderful Major has gone to join them. Even today, I think fondly of our amazing fire horse named Major in endless, cool green pastures, giving "real cowboy rides" to children in heaven.

To our beloved Major we dedicate this wonderful short story.

Good-bye, and God bless you, Major. You are dearly missed, old friend!

Dave   Barbara   Blaze   Dottie

1
Nicklaus Hollyday

That icy winter of 1890 brought another dark, snowy night to the city of Markford, Connecticut. Just a faint outline of the old, faded brick building known as the "City of Markford Children's Orphanage" could be seen through the heavy, white snow as it fell silently downward on this frosty Christmas Eve. Even with the dim wall lantern illuminating the growing snowdrifts and frigid winter air, tonight the orphanage, somehow, seemed even colder than ever.

Under the roof of the building's portico, the cold door ring knocked three times against the dark, heavy door: *tenk, tenk, tenk.*

And then, alone on the snow-covered wooden steps, sat a weathered and broken wicker basket. On one side, a torn strip of worn and faded blue cloth had been tied to the wicker in a limp and pathetically drooping bow. Lying in the basket was a newborn baby; bundled in rags and a threadbare blanket, shivering with cold, and crying pitifully.

As the huge, wooden door opened, Sister Michelle Marie, dressed in her plain habit, looked out—then straight down—as she lightly covered her mouth with her hand. And then, as she had done many times before, reached down with both arms and lifted the winter-chilled basket holding the whimpering child. Without uttering a word, she turned and carried the suffering infant inside, and closed the door. The single set of footprints in the snow revealed the sad, but very common truth: this baby—like so many babies in the early days—was dropped off at the orphanage by someone so poor they could not afford to care for and raise their child. Because he was found on Christmas Eve, the staff at the institute quickly named the baby boy Nicklaus Hollyday.

"Nick," as he would soon be known, spent all of his growing-up years in that drafty, two-story brick building with its creaky wooden floors, large dining hall, stark classrooms, and upstairs dormitory. For better or for worse, for eighteen years, the City of Markford Children's Orphanage was the place Nick would call *home.*

With so many children and so few adults to care for them, many of the orphans' wants simply went unmet. Yes, their basic needs were provided for— but what a child *needs* and what a child *wants* are two very different things. Life was often harsh, and with such little care and compassion, many struggled to develop a genuine sense of security or belonging.

What many children longed for, but did not receive, was individual attention. Steady guidance. Gentle patience. Thoughtful kindness. A loving . . . *family.*

The institute's headmaster was Mr. Bloomquist, a short, balding man with a greying, black, pointed beard and a deeply chiseled scowl. He had a stiff, rigid gait and a personality to match. Now in his late fifty's, he was a stern and hardened man with one thing in mind: to keep all costs down and run the Markford Orphanage without any frills.

He was known for his favorite sayings: *"Wasteful!" "Too expensive!" "Not in the budget!" "Unnecessary!" "Extravagant!"* And, of course, the ever-popular and often-used, *"No!"*

The well-dressed Mr. Bloomquist was also known for his fine, black-wool, three-piece suits, vest and all, which were perfectly tailored to fit his slightly plump, slightly short body, and were appointed with expensive and beautifully carved, imported pewter buttons.

To finish off his peculiar look, he always carried a dark, ebony wood walking stick with a brass tip and a brass ball handle. As he patrolled the hallways, it was impossible to mistake the sound of his stick hitting the floor as steady as the ticking of a clock with every stride.

While he claimed he thought it made him "look dapper," everyone knew it helped support his always-sour leg. He would also use that pint-sized piece of pompous hardwood to prod children and hit desktops when he got upset. For all of his effort to present himself as a strong man, many saw his inability to empathize with others as his primary weakness.

Mr. Bloomquist believed the basic elements of life were all he was responsible for providing. He felt the orphans at the institute were like a flock of unfed pigeons—an unnecessary burden to the city. He simply had no idea of the opportunity he was missing.

If only he had recognized he had the ability to enrich the lives of these young children, they would not just survive, they would thrive. If only he could see it was within his power to transform Markford's "burden" into Markford's blessing. *If only . . . .*

Meals at the institute were as predictable as clockwork: one serving of porridge and milk at the morning breakfast; at lunch, a dry cheese sandwich, water, and fruit or vegetables when they were in season—brown rice when they were not; and usually, supper consisted of potato soup or beans with salt pork, crackers (made by cooking dollops of leftover porridge and rice on the cast iron stovetop), and a glass of milk.

Soups or stews with savory pieces of meat were only offered rarely, as it was considered an unnecessary extravagance by Mr. Bloomquist, and definitely, *"Not in the budget!"* Even though the local butcher would sometimes offer Mr. Bloomquist deep discounts on meats that would soon spoil, he would answer, "And what price shall you ask for cast-off meat tomorrow?"

And so, every so often, "good meat" (meaning "free meat"), was added to the soup.

Although Jillienne, known as "Cooky" by one and all, was an excellent cook, she was on a tight leash in the kitchen, and it nearly broke her heart to serve up the same, repetitive fare morning, noon, and night. While she baked bread for sandwiches every day, desserts and pastries—her specialty—were cause for celebration, as they were prepared only at Easter and Christmas.

Twice a year, Cooky was in her element, sending the enticing aroma of soft, sticky-sweet cinnamon rolls or brown sugar-and-buttery warm apple pie wafting up and down the corridors; lingering until the anticipation was almost unbearable!

Like the rest of the staff, Cooky didn't respect Mr. Bloomquist—or his strict food limitations. She longed for a day when she would see the children's full, pink cheeks break into smiles of satisfaction and appreciation as they enthusiastically ate the delicious food she prepared for them at every meal!

The children wore hand-me-down clothes—donations from local neighbors, and even from surrounding towns. Winters in Markford were always terribly cold and snowy, and it was very common to see the orphans wearing two— sometimes three—worn and oddly-colored coats, and awkwardly bundled-up with extra wraps pinned around their heads and shoulders to keep warm.

Their shoes were also handed down from neighbors whose children had outgrown them. "New shoes" were never new, and even in the bitter cold, no child at the orphanage was ever spared the discomfort of wearing pre-owned, well-worn, and ill-fitting shoes.

Inside the old structure, the large, sparsely furnished classrooms had high ceilings and hardwood floors; the perfect combination for creating torturous echo chambers. They were cold in the winter and hot in the summer. But, at least the warm weather offered the chance to sit by an open window and daydream—sweet relief from the droning, hollow echoes in the stark classrooms.

The maple-and-cast iron desks were usually too small, with seats too hard and uncomfortable to sit in for long. Even so, the seats by the windows were considered the "best seats in the house," and the older children always found a way—by any means necessary—to claim their prize.

During Markford's harsh winters, even with the windows shut tight, the drafty classrooms were so cold that most of the children wore their coats during class. Imaginations had to work extra hard to dream beyond the ice-frosted glass. At the Markford Orphanage, learning—and even daydreaming—wasn't easy!

The long instruction sessions were made even more insufferable by the serious and stern teachers. Anything fun, simply did not exist. While the faithful sisters cared about the children and were truly dedicated to their teaching, they were just not adequately trained or staffed to manage such large groups of students that were made up of all different ages, a wide range of learning needs, and many behavioral and emotional challenges.

Simply making it through each day without losing control seemed to be their primary goal. It would have been a tough row to hoe for any teacher, even *with* adequate training and support.

Due to the large class sizes, basic instruction was given only in reading, writing, and arithmetic. While many of the children had a natural curiosity and desire to learn, the overworked sisters focused strictly on the *task of teaching* without really nurturing the *love of learning,* and for most of the students, book-learning and memorization simply became another unpleasant chore.

For "inspiration," three words were prominently displayed in each classroom: *"Obedience,"* *"Silence,"* and *"Compliance."* When any disruption was loud enough to be heard outside of the classrooms, Mr. Bloomquist was not far behind, briskly entering to enforce the inspiration by rapping the brass ball of his walking stick on a desk and hissing sharply, *"Obedience! Silence! Compliance!* Without me, *none* of you would have a roof over your head!"

At any given time, sixty to seventy children (known as "wards") of all ages populated the orphanage and filled the male and female dormitories. Babies, youngsters, and adolescents . . . boys and girls alike . . . through no fault of their own . . . none of these unfortunates could escape the cruel truth that they were, indeed, orphans—and this roof over their heads *truly was* the only roof they had.

At the institute, life was filled with all the textures from good to bad, yet many important lessons were learned through the experience of living together day and night. The realities of life were what one learned best at the City of Markford Children's Orphanage.

After breakfast and lunch, yard play times were allowed. But before they were permitted to go outside, the children had to first wash their own tin dishes, cups, and utensils in huge galvanized tubs: swishing them first with a wet rag through the soapy wash water; then dipping them through cold rinse water; drying them quickly with large dish towels made from old, worn-out, cotton bed sheets; and finally, stacking the dishes on heavy wooden shelves, and dropping their dried spoons and forks into galvanized storage buckets.

Even in the massive kitchen designed to accommodate large numbers, this chore was always loud and filled with raucous commotion as some of the older wards helped the younger ones, and many rushed to finish as quickly as possible. The lack of hygiene associated with handling the dishes with germy hands, dirty towels, uncovered coughs, and runny noses that were wiped on sleeves, often contributed to major outbreaks of illness.

There was never a shortage of excitement to get outside to the play yard located behind the building and flanked by many great oaks. While the trees provided beautiful seasonal changes and an abundance of shade, the green grass had been worn away by busy feet many years ago, and the grey-brown soil was compacted to hardpan—not even weeds had much of a chance of growing here.

Still, it was easy to see why the children rushed to get outside. The play equipment in the yard consisted of a four-seat swing, a tall metal slide, two wooden-plank teeter-totters, two rickety wooden wagons, and an old, dirty sandbox with two weathered, wooden rocking horses inside.

And as it goes with musical chairs, there were always more children than toys, and every day, some had to go without. But, children excel at imaginative play, and every day, even with very little to play *with,* their creative imaginations turned this rather barren lot into an outdoor wonderland where they could run and play and laugh out loud with wild *extravagance!*

As the years passed, Nick's life at the institute was very basic but fairly stable. He was naturally bright, and learned quickly. Regardless of his environment, he learned a great deal, not only academically, but also how to treat people . . . and how *not* to treat people.

From a very early age it was apparent that Nick had a kind of charisma about him. He was quick to flash an easy smile, and had the kind of warm, outgoing personality that people are drawn to. In fact, Nick had the early characteristics of a strong leader—he was responsible and trustworthy, and had little patience for the "pecking order" system which was all too prevalent among many of the other wards.

Nick was a ready friend, and he had no problem siding with an underdog when it was the right thing to do. His strong character was recognized by his peers and the orphanage staff alike—except, it seemed, for Mr. Bloomquist.

Nick continued to grow, and he developed a "special way" with animals. Maybe it was his gentle manner. Maybe it was his steady patience. Maybe it was the small pieces of bread and cheese in his pockets . . . .

Regardless, animals seemed to flock to Nicklaus Hollyday as readily as people did. He shared his love of animals with the institute's maintenance man, Spike, and they became fast friends. One day, Nick and Spike found a fragile baby squirrel that had fallen from its nest in one of the big oak trees. Without their help, it would have surely died.

They named him Oscar, and with Spike's help, Nick cared for and raised little Oscar, who became the pride of the orphanage. Nursed back to health with warmth, nourishment, and love, the little guy was full of life. To entertain the children, Nick taught Oscar some simple tricks like sitting up for food, and scampering up Nick's sleeve and perching on his shoulder! All the children loved little Oscar, and many of them would clap and cheer and squeal with laughter and delight whenever he performed for them!

Even then, Nick had a deep sense of satisfaction when he felt he was making a difference by providing a few happy moments to brighten the days of those who were so accustomed to their simple and monotonous routine.

Always curious, Nick would marvel at how Spike could repair anything that needed fixing, and he learned many practical skills from Spike. Every chance he could, Nick spent time with him and, as it turned out, Spike's "hands-on" way of teaching was exactly how Nick learned best—a far cry from the institute's boring textbooks and frigid classrooms! Nick loved the challenge of figuring out how mechanical things worked, and he found this kind of learning much more interesting and rewarding.

He also learned that Spike earned his nickname from his wife, Emmy, because she so often found large, spike nails and horseshoe nails tucked into the front bib-pocket of his overalls before she washed them!

Nick especially admired Spike's horsemanship skills with the orphanage's only horse, Sam, a big horse used to pull the orphanage's supply wagon. Because they knew Nick was conscientious, he was the only one the staff trusted to take care of Sam, the tall, brown Belgian draft horse of 17 hands in height. (*Hands* is a term used for measuring horses from the ground to the shoulders, or withers, and is equal to four inches.) Sam was a gentle horse, well over fifteen years old, who was very quiet and good with the children when they stopped to give him a pat or two.

Nick was developing into a fine and capable young man, and as he continued to grow, so did his duties at the institute. Before long, it seemed there was very little around the orphanage that Nick couldn't do or fix.

Nick also fed and cared for Chucky, the beautiful and loyal four-year-old black Labrador with a white spot on his chest. Chucky was stocky and stout—just as a Labrador should be—and gave everyone a sense of protection with his impressive bark! Chucky was also very good for the children at the orphanage. He waited faithfully for them to come outdoors, and could always be found ready for a game of fetch. For many wards, playing with Chucky was one of the only happy things they could enjoy.

Nick made sure it looked like hard work to care for Sam and Chucky when Mr. Bloomquist was around, but if truth be known, he loved every minute he had with the animals, and he felt lucky he was the one they counted on.

The fading, white words, *"Markford F.D.,"* were still faintly visible on the sideboard of the old, retired, red fire wagon that had been donated to the orphanage long ago. It had been used for years to pick up food and supplies in town, but now, because of its advanced age, always seemed to require some type of repair.

Without Spike and Nick, she would have been put out to pasture long ago, but together they kept her running—a money-saving bonus that didn't go unnoticed by Mr. Bloomquist. Because it was in Mr. Bloomquist's financial best interest, Nick was often allowed to help Spike fuss with the wagon, and go with him on his trips to town to pick up supplies. Nick learned how to properly harness Sam to the wagon, where to allow some slack and where to keep the harness tight, how to  connect the lead chains, hook up the lines, and how to drive a horse in harness.

One time, as Spike made the final preparations for a trip into Markford, he told Nick, "Yep . . . this ol' wagon, she jes' need a little more attention an' a little sweet-talk to keep her rollin,' an' she'll go anywhere we ask her to."

And with a gentle shake of the reins and Spike's familiar, ***"Git up, Sam,"*** the wagon was set in motion with the two friends laughing and Chucky barking excitedly and running along beside. On the way to the store Spike stopped at the fire house, took Nick inside, and introduced Nick to the firemen who were on duty.

At the country store, Nick helped Spike load sacks of brown rice, flour, cases of eggs, and large bricks of cheese wrapped in wax paper. On the way home, Spike gave Nick another valuable lesson on how to drive a horse and wagon. Nick noticed how gentle Spike was with Sam; how the slightest pull on the lines would cause Sam to turn or stop. Nick never grew tired of watching and learning from Spike. He looked forward to the day when it would be *his* turn to hold the reins and drive the wagon on his own.

2
May Day

For as long as anyone could remember, there had always been a special bond between the Markford Orphanage and the Markford Fire Department. Both big, brick structures were about a half-mile apart on the same road, and many years ago Markford's Fire Chief, Jacob Henry, had also been a ward at the orphanage.

It was no coincidence that Chief Henry had a special compassion for the children there. Especially at Christmas time.

City budgets were always lean, and tightfisted Mr. Bloomquist never went a penny over budget. Even if there *was* extra money, and he *could* afford to buy Christmas presents for the children, he wouldn't. Since donated clothes and toys were free, the pint-sized miser decided that buying brand-new ones was simply, "Wasteful," and any store-bought decorations or candy were clearly, "Unnecessary!"

It was well-known throughout the area: *any* Christmas celebration for the children at the orphanage was due to the firemen of Markford.

For years, the men of the fire department had provided presents for the children at Christmas time. Throughout the year, the people of Markford would drop off unwanted clothes and old, broken toys at the firehouse and, in their spare time, the firemen would clean and repair them as Christmas gifts for the orphaned children.

Nick had always looked forward to Christmas, and had special memories of the firemen delivering the clothes and colorful toys in their bright-red fire wagons. And some years before, Spike and Nick established a tradition of their own to add to the festivities.

The two would hitch Sam to the old, retired fire wagon and drive into the nearby woods to cut a pine Christmas tree for the orphanage. With a little help from Spike and Nicklaus Hollyday, every year the firemen showcased their gifts of kindness and generosity under a beautiful Christmas tree, with its crisp, pine scent filling the great hall!

As the firemen would bring in the clothes and toys and place them around the beautiful tree strung with paper chains and dotted with simple decorations made by the children, Cooky would bring out tray after tray of her delicious Christmas treats, making it a truly special and happy time for all! Yes, there was an unmistakable bond between the City of Markford Children's Orphanage and the Markford Fire Department—Especially at Christmas!

At age eighteen, Nick had grown in many ways, but it was impossible not to notice that he was also much taller and stronger. Orphanage rules allowed each ward to complete eighteen years at the institute, and with his nineteenth birthday approaching in December, the end of 1909 would mark Nick's final year there.

It was no secret that Nick dreamed of being a fireman, and as he began to seriously consider his future beyond the orphanage, it was only natural that he imagined himself working for the Markford Fire Department.

It was apple season in Connecticut, and one day Nick was in the kitchen collecting the apple peelings Cooky had been saving for Sam. Cooky offered Nick a slice of apple as they talked, and Nick told her of his lifelong dream of becoming a Markford fireman.

And that night, Cooky told her husband, who just happened to know Chief Henry very well.

After hearing the great recommendation about Nick, Chief Henry came to the orphanage to talk to him personally. Together with his large size, likeable personality, responsible character, and practical knowledge, Nick made quite an impression. Chief Henry knew right away that Nick would be a great fireman, and a valuable member of the Markford Fire Department.

And so it was that Nicklaus Hollyday—one of the first African American firefighters in Connecticut—was called to service as a Markford fireman, and his training would begin in about two weeks!

With his nineteenth birthday just three months away, Nick was preparing for his next big step. While he was thrilled with the possibility of working for the Fire Department and ready to leave the orphanage, he was surprised that both delight and doubt filled his mind about his new adventure.

He was excited about this opportunity to achieve what he had always dreamed of—yet somehow, he felt a little anxious about leaving the security of all he had ever known.

Nick's new-found feeling of independence was certainly tempered by the sense of increased responsibility, and for the first time, he fully understood the serious realities of making it on his own.

Then, on a warm and sunny September morning, a nurse-in-training from the City of Markford arrived at the orphanage as a ward nurse. Many at the institute clamored to see the new arrival—and so did Nick. As her wagon stopped, he cupped his hands around the brim of his flat cap to block the sun and better see her.

As his eyes adjusted to the bright light, his natural smile went flat and he swallowed hard just at the sight of her! In her long, white, embroidered dress and wide-brimmed white hat, she put off a glow as though the sun shone from within her!

Her name was May Brown. At age eighteen, she was small in stature, but big in natural beauty. Smart, compassionate, and friendly, May was immediately the bright star of the orphanage. Nick fell for her as soon as he saw her, and he knew he would never forget this day.

It seemed that May had an intuitive ability to attend to the needs of others. It didn't take her long to figure out that not everyone who wanted *her attention* actually needed *a nurse.* In rapid succession, and in her knowing way, she was able to administer doses of caring concern that were surely more effective than simple medicine!

She had all the kindness and love that the impersonal orphanage did not have, and somehow, the more she gave, the more she had to give. It seemed everyone wanted to spend time with someone who was such a genuine joy to be with. And Nick was no exception.

Not fully understanding all the feelings that were wrestling inside him at the same time, Nick was trying to sort out and make sense of what was going on in his head *and* in his heart. He felt happier than he ever had, and an inside feeling of excitement and desire filled him like it never had.

Even with some unanswered questions, Nick was suddenly looking forward to the future, a future that he hoped—somehow—included May Brown!

Now, as it has always been, many young men sometimes feel they have a lack of knowledge on how to approach a young woman they care about. It seems there are always questions, but nobody to turn to for advice—especially when you're an orphan. But Nick was lucky. He had Spike to turn to.

After a few days, Nick told his friend about the special feelings he had for May. He was lost for words and had no idea how to get May's interest. Spike, a man of few words but many insightful feelings, told Nick, "You go be yourself an' git to know that girl—an' things'll be okay. You jes' take your time with her. You talk to her an' do good things for her. You speak the honest truth with her. You be honest with yourself *an'* with her."

"Relationships, they can take a little time, but you let her know she can trust you. An' then when you know each other better, you'll tell her how you feel. You'll show her you're a leader who will take care of her. You'll let her know she is special in all the world."

Then and there, Nick made himself a promise that he would get to know May.

Just by chance, the very next day while working with Spike on the old fire wagon, Nick cut his finger. In general, not really a bad cut, but just bad enough that it could use a bandage. Nick said to Spike, "Maybe I should go upstairs and get it looked at."

Spike said, "Mmm hmmm. Maybe you should." And as Nick bounded off, Spike tucked his thumbs into the straps of his bib overalls and leaned back and laughed.

Upstairs in the First Aid Office, May was, as usual, her warm, wonderful self. Even in her starched nursing apron, she was talkative and caring as she cleaned and bandaged Nick's injured finger. He found it so easy to talk with May, it seemed he'd always known her, and he couldn't believe that just moments before he was so nervous he could hardly approach her!

Just as Nick began to relax and be lulled by May's caring tone and warm smile, Mr. Bloomquist burst through the squeaky door and jabbed his walking stick into the floor, startling Nick and making him jump!

Nick received a scowling stare from Mr. Bloomquist, which was immediately eased by May's warm, "Well, hello!" to Mr. Bloomquist. Nick looked at May, held up his bandaged finger and said, "Thank you."

As he excused himself and headed back to Spike's shop, Nicklaus Hollyday smiled from ear to ear and said, *"Thank you, May Brown!"*

The next day, Thursday, the mail wagon stopped with the morning deliveries. Nick tried to be patient while Mr. Paul, the mailman, sorted the stack slowly.

"Let's see . . ." said Mr. Paul, in his characteristic, painfully slow style. "Looks like these are for the orphanage . . ." he continued, now leisurely reading the delivery name on each envelope. "And . . . this one . . . is for . . . *you.*"

As Mr. Paul's mail wagon rolled away, Nick excitedly opened the envelope addressed to him from the Markford Fire Department. He read out loud, "Report to the Markford Fire Department on Monday morning at eight o'clock to *begin training!*"

Nick smacked the note against his open hand and, laughing out loud, exclaimed, *"Ha haaa . . . ! Yes sir! Eight o'clock!"*

Still holding the note, Nick took off his flat cap, his face growing serious. He slowly began to wipe his brow with the sleeve of his shirt as he came to the realization that this only left the weekend to get to know May better!

Again, Nick asked his friend for advice. As usual, Spike was ready to help and suggested a picnic with May. As he brushed Sam, Spike told Nick, "You git some help from Cooky—see if she'll pack you up some lunch. You go git big Sam washed up nice, clean up that ol' fire wagon, an' take May to the Pine Glen picnic grounds."

All the caring feelings that had welled up inside Nick for years had found an outlet, and they all went to May Brown! On Friday, Nick asked May if she would like to join him for a Saturday picnic at Pine Glen, and he was thrilled when she smiled and said, "Yes!"

Nick was "all flash" as he went about putting together everything for the big Saturday afternoon picnic. Between his other orphanage chores, he cleaned up the old fire wagon, gave big Sam *and* Chucky a bath, and cleaned and polished Sam's harness.

Nick was up early Saturday morning and thinking only of his picnic with May. Cooky made up a hearty, yet familiar lunch, and looking over her shoulder to make sure Mr. Bloomquist was nowhere in sight, she added a couple of extra apples for Sam and a cheese sandwich for Chucky!

Hooking up Sam to the old fire wagon, Nick was glad to be alive, and thankful for all that was right in his world: beginning his new job at the Markford Fire Department; his day at Pine Glen; and the picnic he would share with an angel.

Somehow, Mr. Bloomquist,—stick in hand—found out about the picnic. In a terse conversation with May before Nick arrived, he forbade her to go with Nick because of, "city rules not allowing staff to gather off-site with the wards."

So, as Nick arrived with well-groomed Sam pulling the tidy old wagon to pick up May, she was upset and almost in tears as she told Nick of Mr. Bloomquist's rule not allowing employees to associate with orphanage wards. Nick stood right up in the wagon and stated he was no longer a ward of the orphanage—he was now a Markford fireman!

With his arm outstretched to assist her, Nick took May by the hand, looked into her eyes, and said loudly, *"Climb aboard, May!"* and off they drove to Pine Glen. Sam held his mighty head high in the air, trotting down the road smoother than ever, and Chucky was running along beside, barking. The sun was bright and the autumn day was warm; it was truly a perfect day for a picnic!

On the way to Pine Glen, Nick was so "taken" by May that he had to remind himself of what Spike had told him: *"Be yourself, an' things'll be okay."* So, Nick stayed himself (not such a hard thing to do when you're as real as Nick).

He shared with May his true feelings of happiness and gratitude on being selected to join the Markford Fire Department. May said, "I'm so excited for you, Nick. You must be very proud of yourself."

Proud. That was exactly how he felt. *Proud!*

At Pine Glen, Nick led Sam to a shady spot and fed him the apples Cooky sent along. While Sam munched, Nick watched with quiet amazement as May spread the blanket, set out their picnic lunch, and somehow transformed the ordinary into nothing short of magical.

Alongside May's beautifully embroidered napkins, Cooky's lunch had never looked as good as it did this day. And as they settled in with their cheese sandwiches—and each other—it had never tasted as good, either!

Although Nick was used to taking a leadership role at the orphanage, this afternoon was very different. Lying back in the dappled sunlight, surrounded by leaves just beginning to turn and the scent of warm pitch and pine in the air, he was perfectly content just listening to May. To Nick, May's beautiful voice pooled like rich, sweet, honey as she talked about her life, and shared her hopes and dreams of the future.

May Brown was decended from a Southern slave family—her grandfather had been a slave. She was the daughter of Benjamin Brown, a farmer who made sure she understood the importance of hard work and a good education.

Her mother, Nellie, was a cook and very talented seamstress and needle-worker who shared her skills with May. She had two sisters, June and April, and as family was very important to her, she hoped one day to afford to see them more often.

Nick was listening—and smiling—as May shared a special memory of her mother: "Now, my momma, she can stitch needlework just as fine and pretty as a picture. But I remember looking down one day at a patch she sewed on my pocket, and it just looked like a mess of little knots and tiny little chicken-scratch stitches."

"She said to me, *'Child . . . you look from the inside and see what you see.'*"

"And inside my pocket there was a beautiful, perfect flower embroidered where only I could see it! I nearly wore that pocket off my pinafore looking into it all the time!"

May continued, her smile now spilling over into a satisfied laugh, "I remember thinking that no matter what, my pocket was always full because *I knew something special was in there! Hooo!* Yes . . . yes . . . *looking from the inside*—that memory is a blessing from momma that I'll never forget."

Raised poor but happy, May had worked hard to achieve a better life. She received a good, basic school education, was taught strong family values, and held a deep desire to use her education to help others. Becoming a nurse and having the security of a loving marriage and a family of her own were her lifelong goals.

Like slowly savoring a favorite piece of candy, Nick took his time with May, and he thoroughly enjoyed listening to her. He now knew more about her and was already falling in love. He wondered if it could be possible that someone as special as May could ever fall for him . . . .

They had a wonderful day together, and time seemed to pass way too quickly at Pine Glen. As the sun began to lower in the sky and the early-fall air began to chill, Nick was forced to think about getting May back to the orphanage. They loaded the wagon with their blanket and picnic supplies—along with May's sewing bag and a few pine cones and leaves she had collected.

On their ride back, Nick gently reined Sam back to slow the return trip; Chucky, who was beginning to show his age, was now riding in the wagon and sleeping to Sam's slow, rhythmic clopping.

Together on the old fire wagon, the sun setting at their backs, May was sitting close to Nick, and his heart soared as she clutched his arm tightly. Nick finally opened up, telling May what he was thinking and what he wanted from life. Seemed they both had a great deal in common and very similar goals.

As they turned into the orphanage driveway, Mr. Bloomquist was waiting under the portico on the steps—the very same wooden steps where Nick had been abandoned almost nineteen years ago. Nick pulled up and stopped the wagon right in front of Mr. Bloomquist. Nick nodded at him, and waited for him to comment.

In his harshest voice, Mr. Bloomquist, jabbing his walking stick on the porch to punctuate his anger, stated his distaste for what had happened and charged that May had *intentionally* disobeyed his orders! Chucky growled and barked at Mr. Bloomquist, then jumped from the wagon and headed for the stable.

Nick stood again, slowly this time, and challenged Mr. Bloomquist with a new sense of self-confidence, pride, and belonging. He firmly stated that he was no longer a ward of the orphanage—he was now a Markford fireman, so May did *not* disobey him or break any rules!

Mr. Bloomquist grumbled as he walked away, jabbing his walking stick on the porch. To ease the tension of the moment—and May's concern—Nick winked at May and followed it up with a long, slow smile as he offered her his hand.

On Sunday, Nick and May spent the whole day together talking and walking along the orphanage's paths and driveway, with loyal Chucky following them closely. May seemed to be falling for Nick, as well.

As they walked past the barn, Spike was there shoeing Sam. Nick and May stopped to watch Spike perfectly fit the huge, metal horseshoe onto Sam's massive hoof and hammer it into place with steady skill.

With her caring heart, it was only natural that May also loved animals and, without much thought as she and Nick talked, they both began to groom and brush Sam. It was easy to see the satisfaction and contentment in Sam's half-shut, sleepy eyes as he thoroughly enjoyed all the attention he was getting.

After two days of spending as much time as they could with one another, things seemed to be falling into place for Nick and May, just as Spike had predicted. As Spike finished shoeing Sam, he took the unused nail from his lips, pushed it into his bib pocket and said his "so-longs"; he was on his way home for a warm supper with Emmy.

And as he began to walk along the familiar dirt path home, Spike tucked his thumbs into his overalls and said wryly, *"Mmm hmmm . . . ."*

As Nick finished his side of grooming, he ducked under Sam's massive neck to help May finish her side. All of a sudden, they abruptly came together, facing each other in a pleasant surprise!

Nick dropped his brush, held May's lovely face in his hands, and gently gave her the kiss he had been longing to share with her. May took a deep breath and returned his kiss.

Wondering what had happened to all of his attention, Sam began nodding and punctuated the moment with a low, rumbling, snort. And now, holding each other around the waist, Nick and May just leaned into one another and laughed!

Hand in hand, Nick and May walked slowly back to the orphanage. Arriving under the portico, Nick opened the big, dark door that was so familiar. "I've had such a wonderful time," said May. She held Nick and gave him a long, caring hug. "I just know you're going to do great tomorrow. I know . . . because I know *you.*"

Suddenly, words that usually came easy for Nick seemed too large to squeeze past the lump in his throat . . . so he just smiled . . . nodded slowly . . . and watched May disappear up the staircase.

As he stood on the porch alone, he was almost overwhelmed by a flood of emotions—and memories—as his eyes gazed around the great hall.

He picked up a small box near the doorway marked *"Nicklaus Hollyday,"* closed the big, heavy door, and headed to Spike and Emmy's to bunk for the night.

3
The Fire Horse

In Markford's very early days, the task of firefighting was not just an unorganized effort—it was downright dangerous! When someone rang the city's fire bell to indicate a fire, men from the community would respond to the "fire house," which was really nothing more than a wooden shed that housed the hand-pulled fire wagon with the pump, the buckets, and some tools.

The unpredictable amount of manpower—or first callers, was a very real concern because the first fire wagons were actually pulled by men, a problem when not enough volunteers showed up to pull the wagon which weighed close to 800 pounds! Many times, men were simply hailed right from the streets to lend a hand hauling the heavy wooden wagons to the fire by following the smoke.

The monumental task of pulling just the hand pumper wagon normally required ten to fifteen men who could last only one or two blocks at a full run. They would then need to be relieved by other men—when there were enough other men available—to continue towing the wagon on to the fire. Sometimes it required up to forty men taking turns just to transport one heavy wooden wagon with iron wheels to the fire!

Whenever it rained or snowed, the streets became dangerously muddy and slippery, and it was next to impossible to move anything—especially those big, heavy fire wagons! Most men were exhausted upon arrival at the fires, requiring even more men to fight the fire by pumping on the engine or holding the hoses, trying to keep the fire confined.

Many times, men fell down and were run over. It is easy to see why there were so many catastrophic fires that destroyed entire cities in the early days—and why there were so many injuries and deaths associated with the earliest attempts at fighting them.

Like other cities in America in the early 1900s, horse power was the driving force behind everything in Markford. Day and night, the streets were filled with all types of horses and horse-drawn rigs used for business and travel, and for transporting people, food, freight, animals, and other goods.

As the wooden cities grew, and more fires were reported, the need arose for larger fire wagons that could haul more hoses, more ladders, and bigger, heavier equipment for longer distances. Men were simply no longer able to pull the added weight of the heavy wagons, so it was a natural progression of the horse power era that the mighty fire horse emerged as the solution.

It was the fire horses pulling the new and well-engineered fire wagons that gave Markford's forefathers the ability to better protect the city and its residents from the ravages of fire. Now—with the athletic fire horse—they could move powerful, heavy fire wagons and equipment to the fires in record time, and due to the advent of steam power, apply hundreds of gallons of water!

Early on, many different breeds of horses were used. When an alarm sounded, the firemen just went to the local stables to get a horse or two, only to find them not "broke" or responsive to commands. Not every horse is cut out to be a fire horse, and it didn't take long for the fire departments to realize that specially qualified and well-trained fire horses would be needed.

The first challenge was finding the perfect horse for this very specialized job— only about one in a hundred would qualify. A horse's age, size, coat, and physical attributes had to meet the selection standards. The horses had to be very strong, well mannered, and compatible and easy with both people and the other horses.

They required large, solid legs, and sturdy feet and hooves for traction to pull the heavy wagons. They needed to be easy to train, able to retain the training, and they had to have calm dispositions—capable of following commands and performing their duties in chaotic, frightening fire environments. Today, we use the term "parade broke" to describe horses that are not excited or spooked when exposed to crowds, noise, other horses and fast, colorful, day-to-day elements. In the early days, the term was simply called, "broke."

The vital fire horses came in all breeds and colors, but a specific breed—the Morgan/Percheron—was the most successful because they were a mix of both draft horse and race horse. They were the correct size—not too big and not too small—and they provided both strength and speed. While all colors were used, the white, along with the black horses were really sought after and considered the best of show. The fire departments made extra efforts to find matching size, color, and breed of horses for each fire wagon.

Both stallions and mares were used, but stallions were preferred due to their strength, durability, and liveliness. To help calm the male horses and make them easier to train and less aggressive, young stallions soon became geldings (a male horse that has been castrated).

Their training started as early as two or three years of age, and it normally took one or two years to get a well-trained fire horse. If all went well, the fire department could have a trained, dependable fire horse by the age of four or five. After some real disappointments with local stable horses, the Markford Fire Department bought its first team of fire horses in 1880. It proved to be a wise investment. Very soon, the department began adding to their stable of horses, and because they needed intensive training and full-time care, they also began hiring full-time firemen to train and care for the horses as well as fight fires.

This required building a new fire house with sleeping quarters for the firemen—and the space required to feed, care for, and house the horses within the department. Each horse had its own stall next to its assigned fire wagon. Each fire house also had a hay loft, harness and repair room, watch room, and of course, a kitchen.

Besides its new fire horses, Markford now had a magnificent fleet of bright red fire wagons with rich gold-leaf lettering and markings—each wagon specifically designed to perform different firefighting duties. On average, there were six different types of horse-drawn wagons that could be dispatched from the department:

The Fire Chief's Buggy, pulled by one horse.

The Steam Engine, pulled by three horses.

The Chemical Wagon, pulled by two horses.

The Hose Wagon, pulled by two horses.

The Firefighter Transport Wagon, pulled by two horses.

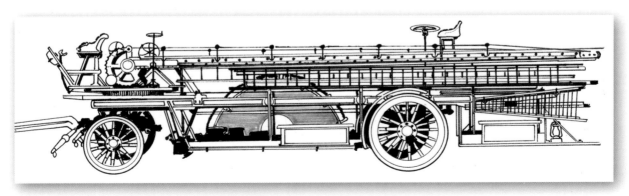

The Hook and Ladder Wagon, pulled by three horses.

The most dangerous part of the job was traveling to the fire. The fire horses were right there out in front, running as hard as they could, pulling heavy fire wagons that did not stop very well. Most fire horse injuries and deaths were caused by traffic accidents. Remember: there were no sirens, stop lights, or red lights; no real laws to control traffic. It was a free-for-all on the early city streets and highways.

There was, of course, the element of living in the same building with horses that had its drawbacks. Anyone who owns a horse will tell you it is a lot of work keeping them happy, healthy, and clean. To control flies, a form of fly paper was developed in the early fire houses, and it was sticky molasses and wax on an old cloth hanging in the stable. All in all, it was worth the effort for the joy they received from these great animals. The firemen of yesteryear would tell you that the extra effort was well worth it. The fire horses were not only the pride of the community, but also of the fire house and all who depended on them to get the firefighting job done.

Firemen and their fire horses formed very tight teams, and when a fire horse was retired, the fireman who was assigned to that particular horse would sometimes buy the horse he was responsible for. Some would also just retire together.

Nothing was sadder than to watch injured fire horses, who had given so much for a fire department, have to be put down. It was just too much for some firemen to watch, so many fire departments had a special policy for such events, and did not involve the caring firemen.

The horse-power era ushered in a glorious chapter of firefighting history where humans depended on the noble and dedicated fire horse. These magnificent creatures were so well-trained, and learned their duties so thoroughly, that many great stories of their legendary performances are still talked about today. They proved themselves to be strong, bright, courageous, and trusted partners—true team members of a worthwhile profession.

Because we asked them to, these heroic animals were able—and willing—to overcome their natural tendency to run from fire and, instead, thunder at a full gallop directly into the face of it! The brave and beloved fire horses of our past endured life-threatening dangers to serve and protect the public. We owe them our heartfelt gratitude, and a respected place in our nation's history.

4
Big Nick

Chief Henry was very fond of Nicklaus Hollyday right from the start. Having also been an orphan and former ward at the orphanage, he appreciated what Nick had to go through as a child, and recognized the hurdles he had overcome.

Without much of a support system, Nick had already beaten odds that had limited many. The fact that he was a self-motivated hard worker and a hands-on quick learner made him a standout rookie fireman.

On October 4th, 1909, Nick reported to duty. He was surprised and somewhat comforted that the fire house was actually quite similar to the orphanage: a big, two-story brick building; the same creaky, wooden floors; a large kitchen and dining hall; and upstairs dormitories where the firemen slept. The differences he noticed immediately were that the fire house was always warm, and delicious, bountiful meals were definitely in the budget!

"Big Nick," as he was soon known by everyone at the department, was a large, strapping young man—well over 220 pounds and taller than most at 6 feet 3 inches. He was strong, capable, and easygoing, and very quickly became a respected and well-liked member of the team.

More than he had ever enjoyed anything, Big Nick enjoyed learning how to be a part of this tight-knit group of men. There was a close camaraderie among them that was easy to recognize and admire, but, for a young man like Nick who had always prided himself on self-reliance, a little less easy to fully understand.

Most of Big Nick's first days at the department were filled with routine duties such as fire training, cleaning and fixing everything that needed repairing, and caring for, grooming, feeding, and cleaning up after the horses. He quickly developed a sense of fire house humor, as the jokes the men played on one another were as much a part of the daily routine as chores!

Taking care of the fire wagons, equipment, horses, and the department's fire dog—a Dalmatian named Blaze—reminded Nick of his years back at the orphanage taking care of Spike's old fire wagon, Sam, and Chucky.

Thanks to his learning experiences with Spike, Nick started at the department as hose man, but was soon driving the fire utility wagon, and he was grateful that his friend had taken the time to teach him those valuable horse care and driving skills.

As a newly hired fireman, Nick had a lot to learn—and not much time to learn it. There were always more fires in Markford during winter, and with the cold season approaching, the department needed to be as prepared as possible as quickly as possible.

Winter would bring shorter days with little sunlight, and long months of cold, icy, darkness. City-wide, the residents had no choice but to illuminate the long periods of inky darkness by lighting open-flame candles and burning oil lamps and lanterns.

Nearly all residences had some kind of fireplace; for many folks, this was how they heated their homes *and* cooked their food. With the freezing-cold Connecticut temperatures on their way, thousands of fireplaces would soon be well-fed and burning hot—crackling loud and sending red-hot embers popping out onto many floors.

As you can imagine, numerous horrific fires were caused by open-front fireplaces!

Many early buildings were constructed poorly, and so close to one another that if one caught fire, the one next to it often burned, as well. Wooden buildings burned so intensely that most were destroyed within minutes, often burning right down to the ground.

Christmas trees in homes were also major causes of winter fires. Along with the beautiful glass baubles or delicate paper ornaments, glittering tinsel, and wrapped candies decorating the trees, it was very common in this era to actually light and burn small candles that were held onto the tree branches with little metal clips!

Countless homes and families were devastated by this very dangerous Christmas tradition.

If they did not perish in the fire, many families were left homeless and out in the cold. There were no organized services in place to help those in need and, typically, the responsibility of caring for the victims of fire fell upon the generosity of Markford's church congregations and neighbors to provide food and shelter.

No wonder winter was always such a difficult time for the firemen of Markford.

As Connecticut's autumn of 1909 gave way to winter and Christmas drew near, Big Nick gained experience on every fire call, and he continued to work every day to learn all he could. He knew that as a firefighter, much would be asked of him.

Even though he had received recognition from Chief Henry for his dedication, hard work, and leadership skills, it was important to Nick that he also measured up to the high standards and goals he had set for himself, as well as those of his peers.

Nick's ability with animals followed him to the department. He had learned all he knew about horses from Spike—and had always admired how Spike could "read" their temperaments, abilities, and habits. Spike had told him that, like humans, some horses were smart and easy to train and handle, while others would take lots of extra work and understanding. And, also like humans, each horse had its own individual personality that was noticeable to anyone who truly knew horses.

And Spike did.

As usual, Nick was a natural with the fire horses. He respected their abilities and loyal service, and very quickly he developed a true love for working with them. Nick watched with amazement each time the horses responded and geared up for fire with precision the moment they recognized the fire alarm.

When the alarm sounded, the stall gate was opened, and each horse was trained to walk to the front of its wagon and back-in, where the harness would be dropped down over its head. A fireman would just hook up three snaps— the collar connector and two driving lines—climb aboard the wagon, and the team was off to the fire, with Blaze leading the pack, barking loudly to clear the way!

During the slow times, Nick was fascinated by the stories he heard about legendary fire horses of the past. He listened carefully, trying to remember every detail so he could share the stories with May.

As he told her one of his favorites, May listened intently as she crocheted Nick a scarf, her knowing hands working the yarn and hook effortlessly. "A long time ago," Nick began, sitting backwards on a wooden chair with an apple in his hand, "there was a faithful old fire horse that wouldn't leave his stall or step out when the fire alarm sounded."

"Now if you know anything about those horses, May, you know that's just not right! The firemen went in there to get that horse out, but even with them yelling commands and tugging on his leads, *he would not move!*"

May's hands slowed as the story intensified. "When they got in the stall," Nick continued, "they found one of the firemen's little sons sound asleep in there, nestled down deep in the warm straw—*right in front of that horse!* If that huge horse had moved even one step forward, that tiny little boy would have been trampled and crushed and hurt for *sure!*"

By now, the yarn and hook sat still in May's lap as she had put both hands up to her ears, and wide-eyed, she looked at Big Nick, shaking her head in amazement!

Fully satisfied with May's reaction to his dramatic storytelling, Nick smiled and took a bite of his apple. Still chewing, he emphasized the tense conclusion by saying, "That's a true story!"

Another story became such a favorite that Nick slapped his leg and laughed every time he heard it. It involved an older fire horse that was so well-trained that he could actually "potty relieve" himself on the scoop shovel when it was placed at his rear!

With all of the December fire activity in Markford and all of the new duties Nick had been learning, he had almost forgotten about his nineteenth birthday—but the other firemen hadn't! On Christmas Eve, while Nick was in the stable tending to the horses, a group of the guys gathered around him.

Dave called out, *"Hey, Big Nick! We got a birthday present for you!"* Nick smiled, and was genuinely surprised. Then, snickers erupted into howls of laughter as Dave pulled the present from behind a post. Decorated with bright red Christmas ribbon, was a brand new scoop shovel!

5
Little Brown House

Big Nick had entered a rewarding profession of honor, tradition, and service—a secure and very sought-after job that many longed for. It provided all the elements of satisfaction for those qualified few who were lucky enough to be chosen: teamwork, organization, discipline, excitement, respect, community service, authority, and security.

Firefighting was a stable job that paid a steady wage. The men were paid around thirty-five dollars a month—pretty good money in the early 1900s. But it was also dangerous and very difficult, not only for the firemen, but for the fire horses, as well. Both the firemen and horses lived and worked at the fire house six to seven days and nights a week, twenty-four hours a day. Normally, the firemen had only one or two days off a month; the horses had no time off at all.

Both city and county open areas were covered by the Markford Fire Department. There were rich areas with well-to-do folks, blue-collar suburbs for the middle class, and the poor slum areas which, in the early 1900s, were unfortunately, far too populated.

Although there were fires all throughout the year, during winter it was not uncommon to have two or three house fires every day or night. There were times when the department was stretched very thin when numerous fires were burning.

Firefighting uniforms were nothing more than cotton shirts and denim pants. The leather boots often got so soaked with water it was hard to walk. Their leather helmets and long, cotton and leather coats did provide some protection, but the coats could soak up water like a sponge, and the cold and snow brought added chilling misery.

Early fire hose was made of cotton and, sometimes, leather. The hose was very hard to handle in cold weather, and would sometimes burst in the freezing temperatures! In those days, frozen water systems and the slippery, icy conditions were hazards that injured many firemen, fire horses, and the general public, as well.

Days off were a luxury that every firefighter looked forward to. Every day Nick had off, he hoped to spend time with May. After many long days and nights on the job, he looked forward to seeing her and spending slow, relaxed time with her.

But May's schedule was almost as busy as Nick's! She spent her days traveling back and forth between the orphanage and the Markford Hospital, where her nurse's training classes were held. While the coursework was very demanding, her test scores revealed she was near the top of her class, and she was on track to graduate with full certification.

When they couldn't see each other during time off, they made the best of the time they had. Following a long-standing tradition within the department, the wives and special ladies of the on-duty firemen brought dinner or desserts to feed the firemen on Friday's. When she could, May would stop by with one of her specialty pies.

Now, some women are famous for their fried chicken. Or, maybe their potato salad. Even their chocolate layer cake. May Brown was known for her prize-winning pies. She baked the most beautiful and delicious pies anyone had ever seen or tasted! She had learned and mastered a few secrets early on from her mother, Nellie. And, while she was very good at keeping those family baking

secrets, May looked forward to the day when she could pass those secrets along to a daughter of her own.

With summer's bountiful harvest, May baked cherry and berry pies; during the fall, May brought Nick's favorite—apple-cinnamon pie! As the cold months settled in, she made custard-based pies like sweet potato pie and pumpkin pie.

Nick's mouth often watered for his own slice of one of May's specialty pies. But his heart swelled with pride as he served slice after slice to his crewmates as they held up their plates, asking for a slice of *"the best in the county!"*

He knew something they didn't know. He knew that even if he served every single piece, May would bake a whole pie for him alone, if he asked her to.

Since leaving the orphanage, Nick had been lucky enough to spend his nights off in Spike and Emmy's spare bunk. Each month after receiving his wages, Nick took great pride and pleasure in bringing some groceries and an envelope holding a few dollars home to Emmy.

He was grateful that his friends had opened their home to him, and even though Emmy told Nick, "We don't need no pay for *nothin'!*" month after month, the groceries and the envelope still came.

By November of 1911, Nick and May were a very happy couple—even though it seemed they never had a chance to spend the kind of time together that both of them wished for. Sometimes, it's the hoping and wishing that draws a couple closer.

It was almost Thanksgiving, and Nick, smiling from ear to ear, burst into Spike and Emmy's with an armload of groceries and goodies. "Now, what's all this?" asked Emmy.

"It's Thanksgiving!" said Nick.

The tabletop was quickly filled as Nick laid out bags of flour, salt, and sugar; a box of eggs; some nuts and candies; and even a smoked ham! In all the excitement, Nick couldn't help smiling as he told his friends about a little brown house he'd just laid his eyes on—not far from headquarters—that had just been posted for sale!

"I've been saving," Nick told Spike and Emmy, earnestly. "Putting money away every month for over a year now. It'll need some fixin', for sure, but if I can get it for the right price, I think it could be something."

Slowly nodding, Spike said, "Mmm hmmm . . . ."

"You two have been real good to me," said Nick. "I didn't have nowheres' else to go—and you two took me in. I'm blessed to have good friends like you, and I know it."

He went to Emmy and wrapped his strong arms around her in a big, gentle hug that surrounded her like a cocoon. Speaking softly in her ear, Nick whispered, *"Thank you, Emmy, for everything."*

Emmy hugged Nick tight and tenderly said back, "Wouldn't-a missed it for *nothin'!"* And now, sniffling and choking back tears, she shooed Nick out of the kitchen, saying, "You go on now, while I put these things away."

She busied herself looking in the cupboard for her finest dish. When she'd found the one that suited her, she wiped out the little glass bowl with her long apron, and then wiped her eyes. Shaking her head slowly in wonderment, she carefully poured a bowlful of the beautiful little candies that shone like brightly colored jewels.

Nick approached Spike. "I don't know how I can ever thank . . ."

Spike interrupted him, and holding the top of Nick's shoulder firmly with his well-worn hand said, "You're a good man, Nick. You always has been—you always will be. An' ev'ry day, I'm awful proud'a ya."

Nick and Spike slapped each other's backs, as Emmy, smiling at the two of them, proudly brought in the lovely dish of candy.

Nick bought the little brown house right in the middle of December—the department's busiest and most hectic time of the year. By the time he was finally able to show it to May, it was December 20th. By four-thirty in the afternoon, the sky was already turning grey as the two excitedly tromped through the un-shoveled snow on the way up the front walk.

Inside, the little brown house was dark. And cold. And empty. And their voices echoed against the hardwood floors. And, of course, May said, *"It's beautiful!"*

Nick held May's hand as he excitedly walked her from room to room, which didn't take long! They came around a corner to the small dining room, where a table and chairs should be. Instead, a Christmas tree filled the space, decorated with candy canes and pine cones tied on with string.

May was giggling as she admired the tree, telling Nick, "That is one fine tree, Mr. Hollyday. But you're going to need a little furniture to go with it! Let's see—you'll need a couple of chairs over there, and you need a . . ."

Nick gently interrupted May, taking both of her hands in his. "I need you, May Brown. I never needed *nobody* before, but *I . . . need . . . you."* He looked right into her beautiful, brown eyes and watched them well up with tears as he knelt down and asked, "Make this house *our* home, May. Please marry me."

May threw herself into Nick's arms saying, *"Yes!"* But . . . Nick was still kneeling, and the unexpected and unsteady motion sent both of them tumbling over like a sack of spuds, almost bringing the tree down on top of them!

Their special moment was showered with laughter, and kisses, and *"I love you's"* —and a few pine cones and candy canes!

6
The Wedding

Markford was growing, and Nick's busy work schedule became even busier than ever. May was making important contributions in the community, training others on how to fight illness and prevent disease through better hygiene practices. She even made some headway at the orphanage—encouraging more hand-washing—especially after using the bathroom and before eating.

Cooky gladly partnered with May to change the way the dishes were done, making sure that after washing and rinsing, Cooky and the novice Sisters dipped all of the dishes and utensils into boiling hot water after every meal.

On Thursday, April 4th, Nellie Brown opened her weathered, wooden mailbox and found a letter postmarked from Connecticut. Inside was a familiar letter from May with news of Markford and her nursing classes, and—as usual—some mention of Nick.

She knew this was no ordinary letter, however, when she saw that the last page was different from the others. It was a wedding invitation! Filled with joy for her daughter, Nellie excitedly showed the invitation to her husband, Ben.

The wedding invitation requested their presence on Saturday, June 22nd, 1912, at the Pine Glen Park in Markford, Connecticut. *"I know it will be difficult,"* wrote May, *"but it would mean so much if you could arrive a day early, on Friday."*

There was much to get done—and time was passing so quickly! Every chance he could, Nick was making repairs to the little house he would soon share with May. And even while she studied for her final exams, May continued to work on the dress she started last December. Her capable hands seemed to have a mind of their own as they hooked and looped the white thread with precision.

The orphanage was abuzz about the upcoming wedding, as many of the staff and wards alike were fond of both Nick *and* May. Between tending to bumps, bruises, and a few sick kids, May heard lots of congratulations and excited chatter about the big day. Except from Kathryn—a young ward who had long ago won May's heart.

Because she was so quiet, no one thought much about Kathryn. But May did. Kathryn loved to write, and when she would hold up a paper to May filled with her beautiful penmanship and fanciful words, May would always ask, "May I read it aloud?"

Nodding yes, Kathryn would shyly smile as May read her stories and poems with interest and dramatic flair. Because May had always been so kind to her, Kathryn created a special poem for a wedding card she was making for Nick and May:

We're All Together
Here Today,
To Celebrate The Marriage
of Nick and May.
The Sun is Bright
The Sky is Clear,
A day Filled With Joy
For Everyone Here!

Love, Kathryn

With her family far away, May was glad to have Emmy's help as the wedding day approached. The two were spending more time together planning the menu and taking care of all the details that matter to a bride. One day at Emmy's the two gathered up the few items of Nick's that were still at the house.

"What about this?" asked Emmy, pulling a small, dusty box marked, *"Nicklaus Hollyday"* from under Nick's bunk.

Wiping the dust away from Nick's name, May slowly looked inside the shabby little box. She was surprised to find only a tattered change of clothes, a worn pair of shoes, and an old, discolored piece of note card paper, folded in half. As she gently lifted the paper, a raggedy strip of blue cloth fell into the rumpled clothes. On the note card were very few words:

May touched the strip of cloth, then carefully placed it back in the folded note card and tenderly tucked them both back into the little box. "I'll take it, Emmy," she said. The two friends finished packing, and took the load of Nick's items to the little brown house.

As the two continued making plans, they thought of asking Cooky if she would bake the cake. Cooky was thrilled to be a part of the special day, promising to bake delicious sheet cakes that she would frost at Pine Glen. Emmy asked everyone she knew not to cut flowers from their gardens until after June 22nd—so they could use them for the wedding!

It would be a grueling 750-mile steam train ride from South Carolina for the Brown family; Ben and Nellie, and May's two younger sisters, June and April. And it would not be cheap. The cost of the train ride was over ten dollars per person—a real financial consideration for a farming family in 1912.

It was also a real sacrifice for the family to give up such a large amount of time during the growing season. The Brown's were grateful to have family, friends, and farmhands caring for the crops while they were gone, but more than once on the trip, Nellie could tell what Ben was thinking, and tried to calm and reassure him with the words, "It'll be alright, Ben. It'll be alright."

After several days on the train, the weary travelers arrived on Friday morning. Big Nick met them at the station, and after quick introductions and hurried hugs and handshakes, Nick wasted no time getting May's bedraggled family and their bags loaded onto the wagon. He clapped his hands once, then rubbed them together briskly as he checked to make sure he had everything aboard. "Everyone ready to go?" asked Nick, climbing aboard.

The confused group looked at one another, then looked at Nick and asked him the obvious. "Well . . . *where is May?*"

Taking his own seat, Nick said with a mischievous grin, "She's . . . *uhh . . . waiting* for you!" With his grin now spreading into a full, wide smile, Nick snapped the reins and said, ***"Git up!"*** He set the wagon in motion with a fast-forward jerk that had Nellie holding onto the wooden seat with one hand—and her hat with the other!

So used to maneuvering the big steam fire engine through the town of Markford, Nick was right at home driving the fast, black horse and lightweight Vis-A-Vis wagon with May's family aboard. Holding onto his hat, Ben marveled at Nick's horsemanship as the girls shrieked with equal parts of fear and excitement at Nick's fast driving. Still traveling at a full gallop, Nick took a great short-cut through the outskirts of town where all the big trees and fancy homes were.

The wind-whipped group was even more confused when, instead of pulling up to the little brown house they had read about in May's letters, they finally pulled up in front of the Markford Hospital, where a large crowd had gathered on the lawn. Nick quickly helped Nellie and the girls down from the wagon, then hurriedly led them through the crowd to where Spike and Emmy were saving five seats.

They had arrived in time! Still standing, Ben Brown now scanned the crowd until he found the only face that mattered to him. When their eyes met, May—in full nursing uniform—smiled from to ear-to-ear and waved at her father, just as her row of graduates was called to receive their diplomas.

Her name was read aloud, *"May Nellie Brown . . . ."*

May was thrilled knowing that those most dear to her were there to support her on this very special day—and they actually got to see her graduate! As the ceremony ended, May ran squealing toward her family, laughing and hugging them all, and thanking them for coming!

She proudly showed them all her diploma and her nursing pin as they congratulated her. When the joyful noise and energy began to calm down, she went straight to Big Nick to show him her pin more closely.

Nick looked at May and told her how very proud he was of her. Then, holding the pin, he stepped to May's father and said, "Sir . . . I love your daughter." He placed the pin in Ben's hand and squeezed it into a fist around it. He looked straight into Ben Brown's eyes and said, "And I'll take care of her all of my days."

Ben silently nodded at Nick and slowly opened his hand, now admiring the pin that symbolized his daughter's achievement. May walked up to her father, smiling. She tapped and pointed at the correct spot on her collar. And with a father's pride that requires no voice, Ben latched the nursing pin onto the collar of May's nursing uniform.

Friday night was a time for family and food—all of them visiting and eating in the little brown house that was now filled with furniture, and decorated with May's special touches.

Nick could clearly see the makings of May by her mother—a striking image of May. He also found out something he didn't know about the woman he was about to marry. Nick didn't know May could be—*so loud*—as she and the three other women laughed and bustled about, fussing with tomorrow's details.

At one point, June started to tell Nick the all-too-familiar story that made May put her chin in her hand and moan. "May couldn't-a been more'n six years old when she started askin' daddy, *'Daddy, what would you-a called me if I was born in March?'"*

Anxious to hit the punch line, April took the story over, and loudly added, "And Daddy would always say"—April adjusted her facial expression and cleared her throat, now imitating her father's voice—*"But you wasn't, was you?"*

And as it goes with the tradition of telling family stories, they all laughed for the hundredth time while May shook her head and rolled her eyes.

Then Ben shrugged knowingly and said matter-of-factly, "Well . . . she wasn't! She was born in May. She's the one that started the name tradition!" And they all laughed again.

Saturday was a glorious day for a wedding. A cool, refreshing morning had given way to a sunlit early-summer day, with white, wispy clouds assuring there would be no rain. Emmy's "flower ladies" had come through with flying colors, bringing buckets and tubs of cut flowers. They provided such a bounty of blossoms that Pine Glen was festooned with the kind of perfect splendor that only God's nature can supply.

May looked beautiful in her white lace gown and veil. She knelt down, quietly telling her flower girl, Kathryn, as she tucked one perfect little flower behind her ear, "I see you from the inside, Kathryn—right into your heart. I know how special you are. The things you are good at, those are *your* special gifts . . ."

And gently stroking the side of Kathryn's head, May continued, ". . . and you make the world a more wonderful place when you share them. Thank you for being here with me today." Kathryn smiled and nodded as they filled the large pockets of her beautifully embroidered pinafore with flower petals. Then the two went to meet May's father.

The old arbor was beautiful; the posts were decorated to the ground with lacy cedar garlands, and a full cedar swag stretched between them. Pine cones and flowers were woven all through the garland, and long streamers of white ribbon followed the cedar serpentine of green—fluttering and flowing with the slightest breeze.

Father Sammon was waiting under the decorated arbor as Nick—in full parade dress uniform—walked the path with his best man, Spike. Now standing proudly and waiting for his bride, Nick couldn't help remembering how he'd fallen in love right here, at Pine Glen.

As Dave's gentle guitar music played, Kathryn walked slowly toward the arbor, making the world a more wonderful place by reaching into her embroidered pocket, and artistically sprinkling the path with sweet-smelling flower petals.

June and April took their places at the side of the arbor, and for the second time in two days, the men in May Brown's life were speechless. Nick watched in silent amazement as May's father walked her down the flowered path. Ben kissed May tenderly on the forehead, and she said quietly, *"Thank you, Daddy."*

May was beautiful in the dress she had made: a crocheted, white lace overlay with a white satin ribbon tied around her fitted waist. Her hair was drawn up in a twisting bun, and her simple veil was attached at the top with a small cluster of fresh, white flowers. She carried a bouquet made for her by her good friend, Emmy.

May looked at the man she would promise to love forever standing beside her in his full parade dress uniform. Seeing the love in his eyes as she held his arm tightly, she knew she would never forget this day.

Father Sammon softened the crowd with a little humor as he prepared to unite one of his favorite young couples in marriage. He then conducted their vows with sincerity, faith, and grace. They placed gold rings on each other's fingers, and made promises of love, honor, and loyalty to one another.

Then, Father Sammon gently opened his Bible, and carefully took out the torn strip of worn and faded blue cloth. He wrapped their wrists together gently, and held their bound hands in his as the three of them bowed their heads and closed their eyes.

In a low, quiet voice of prayerful thanksgiving, Father Sammon said, "We are thankful, Father, that it was *Your* plan to transform 'Hollyday' from a name of circumstance into a name of consequence—a *family* name. For now and forever, bless them, as the two shall be one. Amen."

Unwrapping the cloth, he looked out at the happy crowd, and they started to cheer as he loudly announced, "Nicklaus Hollyday, *you may kiss your bride!*"

The reception at Pine Glen seemed to be the perfect spot. Beautiful trees and flowers, warm weather, wonderful food, plenty of room for the kids to run, and—as promised—the delicious frosted cakes made by Cooky. May and Nick walked the grounds and visited their friends with such a relaxed satisfaction that it seemed they had always been together. As Nick and May glanced over toward the old fire wagon, many fond memories of Sam and Chucky were re-kindled along with other emotions of times past.

Nick and May finally settled at a table with May's family to eat. She knew they would be leaving later today, and she wanted to enjoy them as long as she could. As they savored the reception lunch and special moments of the day, Old Spike presented them with his wedding gift: a sturdy coat tree made from strong Connecticut white oak. Outfitted with long spike nails up and down and all around it, the handmade tree would hold the coats and hats of all who visited the Hollyday house. Spike, with his thumbs tucked into the straps of his overalls, nodded and smiled with pride as everyone admired his craftmanship.

As the afternoon grew long, and with supper time approaching, Cooky and Kathryn headed back to the orphanage, with Cooky wondering out loud, "I wonder what in the world we'll find when we get there—with *Mr. Bloomquist* left in charge!" They both giggled out loud as they went, Kathryn now skipping alongside Cooky.

Time passed quickly, and soon, the party was ending. Nellie and May were rolling and tying newspaper cones around bunches of flowers; bundling them for families to take home. As the wagons were loaded up and the crowd dwindled, the Hollyday's and the Brown's went back to the little brown house so May's family could pack for their train's departure. Nick put away his parade dress uniform, and May carefully folded and packed the dress she had crocheted with love into a box—tucking in the tattered blue strip of cloth.

At the train station, amid smiles—and tears—May and Nick hugged each member of their family—long and slow this time—the kind of hugs that are meant to stay with you awhile. They thanked each one of them for making the long trip to share in their special day. And after they were aboard, Nick and May waved goodbye until the steam train was thundering out of sight.

And then, for the first time as husband and wife, the two were alone. Standing on the loading platform holding hands—alone—*together.*

After a long hug and a tender kiss, Nick softly dabbed the tears from May's eyes with the handkerchief she had made him. Now smiling, May asked, "Today was beautiful, wasn't it?"

Looking right at May, Nick said, "It always will be." Then he gently lifted May Hollyday, and carried her to their wagon.

7
A Major Find

Like Nicklaus Hollyday, "Major" was born around Christmas time. Not in 1890, but twenty years later, in late December of 1910.

Major's father was a large, grey Percheron—a draft horse of 18 hands in height and around 2,000 pounds. He was the center horse of a three-abreast team that pulled a huge, four-row farm plow rig. Major's mother was a well-heeled ex-race horse—a brown Morgan of 15 hands in height. All three horses, along with ten other horses, belonged to a dairy farmer and horse breeder who lived on the outskirts south of Markford where many acres of lush, green land sustained other farms and dairies.

Three months after the wedding, September of 1912 brought beautiful late-summer weather. On a hot afternoon, Nick and his crew were returning from a house fire south of the city. Nick was driving the big steam fire engine when he suddenly saw a young, beautiful white colt running and jumping along the pasture fence line that ran beside the roadway.

Big Nick immediately noticed the fast, smooth, effortless running ability of the young horse. With his flowing, white mane and tail, and strong, agile body, that colt presented such an image that Nick knew he had found something special. He had found the *perfect* fire horse!

Nick quickly turned the steam engine through the farm's gate to get a better look at the colt. He was tall, well-proportioned, all white in color with big hooves, and had a perfect swirl right in the middle of his forehead.

Now, a steam fire engine is not the type of rig that typically just *shows up* on a dairy farm—especially when there's no fire—and with Nick now leaning against the fence, taking his time watching, the farmer was understandably curious!

Since Nick was admiring his horse, the farmer walked over to greet Nick, and gladly gave him information on his prize colt. He told Nick his name was Major; a young Morgan/Percheron of great size for a colt that would just be turning two in December.

Naturally, Nick asked the farmer if Major was for sale. "We're gonna keep him," was the short answer. Due to Major's size, the owner had planned to train Major to be used as a plowing horse on the farm, and he didn't think the young horse would be coming up for sale.

Nick explained to the farmer how Major was perfectly equipped to be a great fire horse, and for added temptation added, "The department would be likely to pay a handsome price for a horse like that. Would you be willing to reconsider?"

After a long pause the farmer said, "Well, I'll give it some thought and keep it in mind, *but . . .*"

But . . . he was shaking his head back and forth with his jaw jutted out sideways, and Nick knew he meant, *"No."*

Nick was sorely disappointed about not being able to buy Major, but he made up his mind right then and there that—sooner or later—he was going to try again to buy Major, and make him one of the best fire horses Markford ever had.

The department now had many fire horses on the roster—fifty-five to be exact—but there were no real shining stars, and there was always a need for extra horses to replace the sick or injured. Nick went right to Chief Henry and told him about Major, and expressed his strong desire to purchase the fine young colt for the department.

Normally, the highest-quality fire horses could cost around two to three hundred dollars—a huge investment and a high price to pay in the early 1900s. Even so, the chief trusted Nick's judgment, and told him to continue trying to purchase Major.

Big Nick often found himself thinking of Major, and envisioning his ideas on how he would train him to be a great fire horse. A goal to be accomplished . . . .

8
The Barn Fire

Later that same year, on a very dark, icy December night, a fire was reported. Nick and the firefighters were called out to a barn fire just south of the city. Upon their arrival, the firefighters found the top, front half of the barn full of fire—burning through the hayloft and heading quickly to the rear.

That night, Nick was assigned to the hook-and-ladder wagon. Nick and the other firemen were met by the frantic farm owner who told them that due to the cold, he had put all of his horses in the barn, and now they were trapped in the fire!

Using their axes and running through the hot inferno of smoke and fire, Nick and his team of firemen eventually had to drop down to their knees and start crawling through the black, billowing smoke that was so dense they could hardly see where they were going!

The intense fire was crackling, and beginning to roar. As the fire grew and the barn fire raged, they could hear the frightened horses desperately kicking the walls and whinnying in the darkness.

As they continued to make their way through the flames and fire, timbers and support beams started falling from the barn ceiling, bringing heavy beams and burning bales of hay crashing down around them, and filling the air with fiery streamers like swirling, red-hot fireworks!

The wide-eyed and terrified horses, still trapped in their stalls, were now screaming and rearing and pawing their hooves wildly on the walls and gates, frantically trying to get away from the fire! The scorched air they were trying to breathe was filled with hot smoke and flying embers!

After many long minutes in that inferno, the firefighters were running out of time! They finally managed to unlatch as many stall gates as they possibly could, releasing and rescuing the colts, fillies, and horses from the rear of the barn—and saving all but two.

After several hours of fighting fire and pumping water vigorously from the steam engine through all the available hose from the hose wagon, the firemen finally had the blaze under control, and were starting to mop-up the smoldering mess.

Although the barn was a total loss, the farm owner was very grateful. As fate would have it, he was the same farmer who had said *"No"* to Nick in September. When he saw Big Nick, he recognized him right away—and remembered that Nick had wanted to buy Major for the fire department.

As it turned out, Major was one of the horses Nick and his crew had just saved! The farmer was so impressed with the trained fire horses, the bright fire wagons, and how hard the dedicated firemen had worked to save his barn and horses, that he told Nick he would donate Major to the Fire Department as a gesture of his thanks.

He told Nick that he was right—with his energetic, bright, lively nature, Major would make a far better fire horse than a slow plow horse, and it would be a real shame to use such a gifted, beautiful horse for such a menial task.

"The only thing I ask," said the farmer, "is that the name stays with him. He was named as a tribute to my father—he was an Army major. And he was a good man—God rest his soul."

Now two years of age, Major was about to have a new home and an exciting new future with the fire department. Nick was thrilled knowing that Major was going to be part of the Markford Fire Department stable! He was certain that this would be a great partnership—one that would suit Major— and suit the department, as well.

Nick imagined Markford would have one of the best fire horses in the world—once *he'd* finished training him!

The next day, Nick arrived at the farm with the fire department's horse van to pick up Major. Full of spunk, as usual, Major sensed something was about to change, and he was more than just a little reluctant to enter the van. Major put on quite a show: running, bucking, and acting up—as well as not responding to Nick or the farmer's commands or tugs; pulling back and standing stiff-legged and wide-eyed. But, after a while, with Nick and the farmer's reassuring pats, he finally settled down and entered the van *his* way; he just wanted to let everyone know who the *boss* was.

Nick was not really surprised by Major's wild reaction to simply entering the van. It was Major's first time in a horse van, which Nick took into consideration. But even so—it was a battle of the wills! And patience paid off. Nick also knew the change from the peaceful, quiet farm life to the hectic, noisy fire house life would take some getting used to for Major. Plus, he knew Major had just experienced the barn fire, and that event alone had some influence on Major's skittish behavior.

All of this was good for Nick to see. He was evaluating Major's actions, and determining what approach was going to be needed to accomplish such a huge training task. Everything was going to change for Major; no more quiet farm life. Now his days would be full of strange sounds, odd smells, colorful images, and many new people to meet.

To successfully establish himself as Major's leader, Nick knew the first thing he had to do was to earn Major's respect and attention. On the way back to the department, Nick was optimistic and looking forward to his future work with Major.

Optimism is a funny thing—it has a tricky way of making a person forget about the realities of a word like—*work.* Nick had been waiting anxiously for a long time to begin training Major. He had already imagined *this* kind of work would be an amazing and exciting opportunity.

But . . . from Major's point of view, new environments could be something to be fearful or cautious of, and clearly, something to be *avoided!* For humans and horses alike, there is a first time to try new things. Even very difficult things.

But, that's how all new training starts . . . .

It was Christmas Eve as Big Nick entered the fire headquarters' back yard with Major in the horse van. The on-duty firemen were already outside, waiting anxiously for Nick's arrival.

When the van pulled in, May rushed outside in her brown, furry shoulder wrap with decorative fur pompoms on the ties, and her furry hand-warming muff. Even Blaze the fire dog came out to meet Big Nick's "prize student."

As Major was led out of the van, everyone knew Nick had made a great choice. He really *had* found the perfect fire horse! Major was truly an amazing specimen: bright white, tall, well-proportioned, with large, broad hooves; he seemed to be all muscle and full of life. Already beginning his training, Big Nick said slowly, *"Hold, Major."* Major stood there as if he knew that everyone was looking at him and talking about him.

And they were!

Even Blaze was nosing around, checking Major out. As the soft December snow started to fall, it looked as if someone had spread out a white welcome carpet for Major and, following a long-standing Hollyday tradition, Major was an awesome Christmas arrival. May was so impressed with the stunning, proud, white horse, she suggested they should name him, *"Christmas Major!"*

And so it was that, "Christmas Major"was officially approved by all who were there that Christmas Eve in 1912.

9
One Major Fire Horse

Major's training started off badly at first. Big Nick *thought* he knew exactly what his early training sessions with Major would and should be like—and what the outcome would be. Nick knew the first thing any horse trainer had to do was get the horse's respect and attention. Now—just how one accomplished that was another matter!

It seemed Major had his own ideas of how his days should be spent. He had a strong personality—and his own agenda—which definitely added a new dimension to Nick's life! At first, Major was very independent, spirited, and wanted to live his life his own way . . . running and jumping all day! He didn't pay any attention to Nick at all.

Nick was trying to get Major accustomed to the bridle, collar, harness, and lead lines, but it seemed Major had other ideas. Major was okay with the bridle, but would not stand still for the collar installation . . . or the harness, for that matter. He did not like the red wagons, and just the *smell* of the steam engine would cause him to be wide-eyed and fight all of Nick's requests!

He didn't like the narrow stalls he was to sleep in, and things were simply not going well at all between Major and Nick. For some reason, Major seemed too easily spooked at all the fire house noise, which was way different from his previous life grazing at the dairy farm.

Maybe that barn fire had set a wrinkle so deep into Major that no amount of training could iron it out. Major seemed OK with people and touching, but he would not go into the fire house; it seemed the smell of fire might be the issue.

After a couple of months into the training, it seemed Nick just wasn't getting anywhere. He was almost ready to throw in the towel. He began to wonder if maybe all of Major's potential was just a little too, well—*potent!*

Over supper with Spike, May, and Emmy, Nick told his old friend Spike about Major's training—or lack of training as the case might be. Spike was flattered when Nick said he could surely use a little insight from, ". . . the best horseman I ever knew."

In early March, Spike stopped by the department to visit with Big Nick and check on his progress with Major.

Nick described the trouble he was having with the lively Major. While Major stood in his outside stall, Spike looked him over—and up and down. He watched his body movements. He watched him for a long time. He listened to the sounds Major made. He even listened to the rhythm of his breathing. He ran his hand across Major's shoulder and down his back, watching Major's reaction. He took major for a walk, and then watched Major for a good while.

After a long period of quiet observation, Spike suggested that Nick try the old *"git with 'im"* method.

Speaking slow and deliberately, Spike said, "Before you train again, you git in that stall with 'im. You take your time with 'im, an' things'll be okay. You jes' sit there an' git to know 'im. Know e'vrything 'bout 'im."

"You talk to 'im an' tell 'im what you're thinkin'. How you think 'bout you an' him together an' what you want from 'im. You try to hear what *he's* tellin' *you.* You feed 'im his food an' treats from your own hand. You groom 'im like he won first prize. Let 'im get a little hungry, take 'im inside, and then you hand feed 'im a little at a time, so he sees you as the feeder and boss. Git' im use to the inside of the fire house first, by rewardin' 'im and comfortin' 'im inside—not outside. Seems the fire house is the issue."

Nick sat motionless, just listening as his wise friend—and favorite teacher—went on.

"Think deep. Talk soft an' clear 'bout what you want 'im to do. Be patient. Stay close. Relationships can take a little time, but you let 'im learn that he can trust you." And now, nodding with assurance, Spike finished with, "Show 'im there's nothin' to be afraid of in that fire house by rewards. An' when you *really* know each other, there'll be a trust there between you two that is special in all the world."

Nick was fascinated by Spike's understanding and knowledge of horses. He was amazed that not once—*not once*—did Spike talk about the physical training which would come later. He was talking about a kind of mental training that connected the spirit of the horse with the expectations of the trainer through mutual respect and trust.

Now, Nick trusted Spike's training advice over everyone's. But even to Nick, expecting Major to read his mind seemed a little hard to believe—but he knew Spike would never steer him wrong. Besides, by now, Nick was ready to try *anything!*

The next day, Big Nick entered Major's outside stall and just sat there, thinking about what Spike had said. Major never looked directly at Nick, but he seemed to sense that something new was going on. There's a first time for everything, and this was their first time working together on a *true partnership.*

Spike would say that's how all *good* training starts . . . .

After some hours of thinking about how he saw Major fully trained and the two of them working together like a well-oiled machine, Nick got up and took Major inside and fed him, using his bare hands to handle the hay and grain.

He started to groom and brush Major's coat, slowly working around to his big, stately head. Nick looked confidently into Major's soulful eyes, telling him all about the magnificent future he would have as the lead horse for the Markford Fire Department.

Big Nick spent all that day with Major in his stall inside the fire house. The next day things seemed to turn around a little. Nick and Major started to have a new understanding of one another, and Major began looking at Nick for the very first time with an understanding eye that Nick easily recognized.

Over the next few days, Nick continued to spend extra time just being with Major: feeding him, grooming him, and talking to him. Leading Major through things Nick wanted him to do. *"Hold, Major"* was the first goal . . . with a small treat as a reward.

By day four, all of a sudden Major seemed to welcome the training—and seemed excited to learn new things. Leading Major around and fitting the harness was much easier now. He was responding more quickly to Nick's verbal command of, *"Hold, Major."*

Major even added a new move of his own. When he lifted his head, Major displayed a natural "smile" that was as real as any human smile! A simple curl of the upper lip produced a bigger-than-life, toothy, horse smile that made Nick laugh out loud!

Now, Major was lining up and pulling the training wagons with little or no effort at all! It was also becoming easy to recognize Major's natural athletic tendency. Even in full-harness, he always wanted to *run,* and Nick often had to really hold Major back.

Nick literally had to walk Major through his training sessions, teaching him the basics such as where to stop in front of the wagon so the harness would drop properly onto him. Then Nick would lead Major to and from the stall, and show him what to do when the alarm bell sounded.

One of Nick's training exercises (when an actual alarm gonged) was to hook Major to the training wagon and follow the real fire wagons to the fire. As Major held his location, he was exposed to the sights, sounds, smells, and activities of the fireground. Nick's goal was to have all of these dynamic, new experiences become a matter of routine for Major.

Three weeks later, it seemed that Major was actually eager to please Nick. Major would bow his big head and give Nick a loving nudge now and then. Nick was thrilled that Major was well on his way to becoming the great fire horse he had been hoping for!

What made a fire horse great was its ability to think and perform what it had been taught to do. Or, in some ways, to even improve the evolution, on its own. Such was Major's ability. Instead of backing into the stall, as Nick was trying to teach him, he just walked in and turned around inside of the stall, much to Nick's amazement! "Stall training completed," exclaimed Nick!

Major became more and more familiar with the many chaotic sounds of the fire house. After a while, he actually seemed to enjoy the excitement and attention created by the crowds, the sight and heat of the fire, and even the smell of smoke; it all added a vivid new dimension to Major's life as a fire horse. Responding to fire calls eventually became stimulating and rewarding events for Major! He was able to recognize the fire house's own fire alarm of 3-2-1 (three gongs, two gongs, and one gong) on the big wall bell. When the 3-2-1 bell rang, Major would stomp, step-up wide-eyed and ears forward, then turning; he was ready . . . .

Major also seemed to appreciate the human contact he had with all who met him. He was truly a friendly horse with a personality to match. When coaxed by Nick, he would not only perform "the Major smile," but many times would also bow his massive head to any person who fed him a treat.

Whenever May came in with a treat for Major, she was greeted with a treat of her own—a vocal whinny hello—along with a bow!

At the young age of four, Major was assigned to headquarters' Steam Engine #1 as the new horse of a big, three-horse hitch that pulled the powerful steam fire engine. He was assigned to the right side, called the "near" horse or wheel horse position of the hitch, as this horse was near the driver, who typically sat on the right side of the big seat. From there, Major worked his way to the left, called the "far" side.

Once he was completely broken-in and showed he could lead the team, Major was advanced to become the lead center horse for the big steamer. Major had exceeded all of Nick's expectations and proved that he could do the job and beyond—setting the example for all the other horses in the fire department.

Through the next year, Big Nick and Major answered many fire calls, and together with Major's team-mates, Ben and Bob—their performance was always spot-on.

After his promotion to driver, Nick drove the horses on the steamer, and Dave was the engineer who ran the steamer's boiler and pump. Nick, Dave, Major, Ben, and Bob went to many fires together and became known as the department's most reliable unit for getting to the fire safely and swiftly, and putting the fires out quickly. They were very proud to be known as the best team in Markford: "Steamer #1."

Finally retired from the orphanage at age eighty-eight, Old Spike loved coming by the department to check in on Nick, the other firefighters, the fire horses, and—of course—Major.

Spike became such a regular at the fire house, that he had a designated chair waiting for him, where he'd sometimes sit for a couple of hours at a time—never seeming to tire of watching the four-legged athletes. Nick's fire house had nine fire horses, four fire wagons, and twelve firemen, so there was always something going on.

Sitting there in little puffs of smoke that smelled of apricots and molasses, Spike would pull short, rhythmic draws on his pipe as he watched. He'd often chuckle and smile and shake his head in amazement when Major performed in his stall.

It was no secret that Major held a special place in Spike's heart. He gazed at that horse with a look of satisfied accomplishment on his face—the kind of look that anyone would love to see on the face of their own proud grandfather.

Major was not only large in size and ability, but that horse had a personality to match! It could be said that Major had a sense of humor—he was actually a bit of a ham! He seemed to know he was funny, and he genuinely enjoyed being a jokester.

When Nick would put a carrot in his back pocket, Major would nudge Nick to one side, bite the carrot and take it out of Nick's pocket! Major also had a fun habit of peeking around the stall post and moving back and forth, checking people out peekaboo-style as they approached the stall.

Half honor student and half class clown, Major could do it all, and it was easy to see why he was the hands-down fire house favorite. But he wasn't just a favorite with Spike and the firefighters at the department—he became beloved by the community children, as well.

On their way to school, Major had a kind of magnetic pull on the children that few could resist. They literally ran to the fire house each morning to see him, offer him a treat, and give him a pat or two.

They cheered and clapped when Big Nick directed him to "smile" and count with his foot!

Major had been known to "voice" his happiness when the children appeared, and he always smiled with gusto after getting his treats and loving pats. Big Nick even taught Major how to tell time—to help prevent the kids from being late to school. When Major stomped three times, it was off to school!

Blaze was also a hometown favorite. Known for her loyal dedication to Major and all the fire horses, she wasn't shy about earning a treat of her own.

She would often sit at full attention "speaking" and even rolling over for her tasty rewards.

Together, Blaze and Major put on quite a show for anyone who stopped by to admire the animal attractions at Markford Fire House #1.

By now, it seemed most everyone had heard of Major and Blaze—their abilities were becoming legendary around Markford. And, like revered team mascots, they had developed a special bond with the entire city.

10
The Big One

Nick and May were comfortably settled into their little brown house. Big Nick, Major, and Blaze were also a well-bonded team, working together with a predictable performance like the perfect pitch connecting with the sweet spot of the bat. Other firemen came from other cities just to check out "Steamer #1."

Their working partnership had truly developed into the well-oiled machine that Nick had envisioned almost three years ago. Major had earned top billing at the fire house—his stable was right up front so he could be the first horse out to the mighty steamer.

The floor of his stall was regularly spread with clean hay and straw, which kept the area warm and padded when Major would lay down for a well-deserved rest. His stable even had a hinged window so he could see outside and get a cooling breeze in the summer!

Faithful Blaze had formed a very strong bond with Major, and she was always near his side—either running along beside the steamer, sitting by him in the stable, or sleeping next to him, nestled down in the warm, clean straw. They ate together, got baths together, and slept together—Blaze's head resting on Major's warm belly on cold winter nights.

Everyone knew that the periods of relative quiet, routine, and even boredom were always followed by frightful times filled with adrenaline, excitement, and fear when the big city fires raged out of control. Knowing fire could happen *at any* time was the reason the firefighters had to be prepared *at all times.*

The true value of planning and practice was being ready to respond at a moment's notice. The firemen specifically trained for the alarm that always seemed to come during the night, when everyone was asleep and warm in bed inside the fire house.

When the huge alarm gong would ring, "3-2-1," the firemen would slide down the fire pole with their bulky gear on, red suspenders and all, run to their positions, snap in the horse harness, and jump on the wagons ready to respond to the fire.

Hooking up the horses took less than a minute, thanks to the hanging "quick" harness which, in a matter of seconds, could be dropped down onto and then hooked to the horse. The collar was snapped, the lines were snapped in, and the ready call was sounded.

The tall fire house doors would swing open, and the chief's buggy would head out— leading all the other fire wagons to the fire— bells clanging, horses stomping, smoke billowing from the big steam fire engine, and Blaze running and barking, leading the way to the fire. Yes, it was quite an exciting sight to see—and something to always be prepared for . . . .

There is a term in the fire service called, *"The Big One."* As you might guess, it means a really big fire—the kind of fire that, unfortunately, Markford experienced about three or four times each year. A fire so large, that it required many firemen and a large number of fire wagons to try to keep it from spreading, and used every resource available just to put it out.

The Big One that happened on Thursday, December 9th, was the kind of fire that would put the firemen's nighttime training to the test. It came in the middle of an extremely cold winter night at about two o'clock in the morning— it was still pitch-black outside. When the alarm sounded, the startled firemen jumped into action.

Flames could already be seen for miles, and the firemen knew they had their work cut out for them. They raced from the fire house, heading straight toward a menacing blaze so large, the eerie orange glow that it cast against the dark sky could be seen city-wide.

On the way to the fire, Big Nick and Major knew this was going to be a difficult night. The fire was in the industrial section of the city in the textile district, next to the Connecticut River. Beastly flames were already roaring out of just about every top window of the three-story, brick building! As they got closer, they could see it was the Markford Coat Factory. The smell of the burning building and the heat from the fire could be felt a great distance away. In no time, the whole town was awakened by the sounds and smells of the big fire.

Major, Ben, and Bob were pulling hard on the heavy steamer, their hooves loudly pounding the roadway with power and strength. The steamer's bell was clanging and smoke was pouring from its boiler! The chief's buggy was leading the steamer, and the hose and hook-and-ladder wagons were closely following.

Upon arrival, the chief found the large, brick building—almost a block long—already half-full of fire. Flames were pouring out of every north-side window! Firemen call this intense kind of burning, "well-involved," and those are exactly the words they used to describe this fire!

The chief immediately sent a runner for more fire wagons.

"Ring out a second and third alarm!" he called. (Each alarm brings: one district chief, one steamer, one hose wagon, and one hook-and-ladder wagon.)

The Chief yelled out commands to the on-scene crews:

"Secure water supply!" (Connect the steamer to a reliable water supply.)

"Big line to the exposures!" (Use large hose lines to wet down the structures next to the building that is on fire to prevent them from burning.)

"Set up master lines!" (Master lines are hose lines so large and heavy they require four to five men to handle the huge amount of water they deliver to the fire.)

Everyone knew exactly what to do. Even Blaze was doing her part, barking excitedly, and chasing off any other dogs that could upset the fire horses.

Firemen were pulling hoses from the hose wagon. Everywhere they could, anxious townsfolk were gathering to watch the action. Some townsmen were lending a helping hand by pulling the cold, heavy hoses where they were directed to.

Big Nick had Major, Ben, and Bob pull the steamer over to the edge of the Connecticut River to draft water into the steamer so the pump could thrust the water back out to fight the fire. (*Drafting water* was a method that literally sucked water from the river into the steamer and, by adding pressure, made it possible to send a continuous, powerful stream of water greater distances—for long periods of time.)

Nick shouted out to Major, **"Hold, Major!"** to hold the steamer in place so the firemen could hook up all the suction and discharge hoses to the steamer. Major responded with an excited whinny, and planted his hooves firmly into the ground, setting the example for Ben and Bob to follow. The steamer was now set solidly in place and prepared for the big pumping operation.

The hose wagon stopped next to the steamer. After the firemen connected the hose to the steamer, the hose wagon driver snapped his whip in the air, and off the hose wagon went toward the big fire, allowing its hose to fall along the ground as a water supply line leading straight from the water supply to the fire.

Dave, the steamer engineer, already had the fire in the boiler hot and ready to produce the steam pressure needed to pump the water onto the fire. Once ready for action, the big steamer was capable of pumping *1,000 gallons of water a minute* onto the fire!

Blaze was right by Nick's feet helping to calm the horses. The firemen on the hook-and-ladder rig assisted the hose wagon crew as they laid the fire hose to the fire.

Dave throttled the big steamer up and started pumping. Smoke and sparks were belching from the enormous boiler, and it was actually shaking the ground from the massive force of its pumping action!

Each discharge line was flowing 250 gallons of water per minute, with three to four firemen holding onto each hose line, directing the water stream onto the flames. The heat from the massive fire was actually powerful enough to warm the chilly night as more fire wagons and firemen arrived, creating the same hectic scene of organized chaos all over again.

More steam engines were in position at the river to draw water, and more firemen were pulling additional hoses. Even though the fire zone looked like mass confusion, everyone knew exactly what they needed to do.

Big Nick disconnected Major, Ben, and Bob from the hot, pumping steamer, and walked them to a safer place behind another building to reduce their exposure to the fire. A little distance from the fire would also help ease their stress of being over-excited for such a long period of time. Faithful Blaze followed along, knowing it was her job to remain with the horses to help protect them and keep them calm.

All of a sudden, there was a deafening crashing sound! The factory roof had caved in, and the walls were crumbling as a large fireball and sparks burst into the night sky! *What a sight*—like thousands of fireworks shot out of a cannon! The entire north side of the building had totally collapsed!

More intense fire was now boiling from the fallen building. Turbulent flames were shooting up and grasping at the factory timbers, hungry to consume all that was around them! As far as the eye could see, towers of smoke rose and the ominous red-orange fire glowed against the black night sky!

The firemen of Markford had a huge job on their hands. After several hours and many hose lines shooting water onto the inferno, the massive fire seemed to ease somewhat, but the firefight went on as the firemen continued to spray water, trying to save whatever they could.

As the heat from the flames began to back down, the winter cold bullied its way to the front again—freezing the far-reaching water streams into thick layers of ice that looked like white frosting poured over the crumbling building. Everywhere there was water, ice started to form.

As the intensity of the fire began to subside, the level of suffering for the firemen actually grew worse. A different kind of misery was moving in. The kind of icy-cold misery that settles in deep and makes you shiver until your muscles cramp and bones ache. A bitter, stinging, cold that makes it painful to bend your fingers.

Even so, the firefighters fought on, directing water onto the burning piles of smoldering rubble and bricks—making sure the fire didn't re-ignite. A long, frigid battle lay ahead for the firemen and fire horses of Markford, Connecticut.

After almost five hours, Nick was wet, freezing cold, and exhausted from fighting the stubborn fire. He took a short break by returning to Dave and the still-pumping, hot steamer to try and warm his hands. It was then that he realized that during all of the commotion, he had completely forgotten to put blankets on the horses! Grabbing the blankets from the back of the steamer's seat where they were already warmed by the boiler, Nick dashed over to where he had secured the team. There they were—Major, Ben, Bob, and Blaze—steadfastly waiting in the freezing cold, standing in ice and snow.

Nick put a pad down for Blaze, her tail wagging, even though she was shivering. She sat on it immediately, licking her lips in appreciation. As the heavy, warm blankets were laid upon the horses, Nick could see their contented relief as they exhaled foggy blasts from their nostrils. Steam began to rise from their massive bodies as a light snow began to fall.

By 7 a.m., the morning sun was trying hard to break through the threatening, grey snow clouds. Here and there a bright spot was peeking through. The snow had finally stopped—but the bitter cold remained.

The smell of burning wood smoke filled the air, and the crowds that had diminished because of the extreme cold now paraded by the building to see the ghoulish spectacle: the huge, burned-out carcass of the destroyed coat factory encased in milky ice and covered with a million icicles that made it look like a jagged, frozen ice fortress.

Most of the firemen had worked straight through the freezing night, and they now gathered together and huddled around any warm spots of fire that remained. Major and the other fire horses were all checked for blankets and brought close together to conserve their body heat.

By 10 a.m., after many brutal hours of fighting fire in the winter cold, the blaze was fairly controlled. The chief decided to release some of the first-alarm wagons, which included Major's steamer. It was finally the best time of any fire call—the time to head back to the fire house and get warm, fed, and rested.

As Nick and Dave were hooking up the team and preparing to head back to the department, Alfred, a fellow fireman came over to Nick and asked him to come and take a look at what they had found in the unburned part of the coat factory.

Along with the others, Nick returned to the building's storage rooms and found crates and crates full of brand new coats and jackets of all sizes—from adult all the way down to very small children's. Some of them were very wet from the water, but none of them were burned or scorched.

Nick immediately wondered if they could be dried out and given to the children at the orphanage. By now, the population of the orphanage had grown to over eighty wards, and there were easily enough unburned coats in the damaged factory for every child to receive one!

As soon as he had a chance, Nick went straight to Chief Henry and made his case; "Chief, none of those coats are really damaged, but if they're going to throw them away because they can't sell them, maybe they'd be willing to donate them to the orphanage. The kids could sure use them . . . ."

Nodding in agreement, Chief Henry knew it was true. He told Big Nick that he would talk to the factory owner as soon as possible, and ask if they would be willing to donate the coats.

By noon, Nick, Major, and the steamer team returned to the fire house, and it was *so* good to get back. Major and the boys were unhooked from the steamer and led to their comfortable stalls filled with sweet, clean straw. Nick gave Major a nice rub-down and toweled him off, while Dave took care of Ben and Bob.

The horses enjoyed a hearty breakfast of oats and grain—and after enjoying her breakfast, it didn't take Blaze long to get comfortably nestled into the deep, warm straw in Major's stall! As usual, Blaze was right next to Major.

Sometimes, it seems, there is no rest for the weary, as Dave then returned to the mighty steamer to ready it for the next alarm. It would take another hour or two to prepare the big machine for the next emergency.

Along with some of the other wives, May had gone to the fire house to follow the news of the big fire, and to help relieve the stress of waiting alone. Together, the women prepared a hot, delicious meal that would be ready when the firemen made it back. They knew from experience that the men would be cold, exhausted, and hungry when they arrived.

Nick was very proud of May, and thankful for her thoughtful concern—not just for himself, but for all of the men in the fire house. No longer a rookie, Nick didn't have to wonder anymore if he really fit in. He remembered how he used to admire the camaraderie he saw between the crew members, and now, he fully understood it.

He had a mature understanding of the close bond between them, and he was proud to consider himself a member of this tight-knit, straight-talking group of men. He knew he was part of a true brotherhood—a group of men who trusted and relied on one another as they willingly put their lives on the line to protect and serve. They were responsible for one another.

Back safely together with his crewmates in the warm fire house—and about to eat the roast beef, potatoes, and gravy that their wives had made with loving care—Big Nick looked into the faces of his fellow dirty, worn-out firefighters, and he knew he had much to be thankful for. Looking forward to a good meal, hot bath, and a warm bed, Nick was happy to be alive.

11
A Big Change

As it was after every fire—even a big one—life at the department began to return to normal very quickly for the firefighters. It had to. It was their job to be ready—the people of Markford were counting on them. To respond with consistency, the firemen were trained to rely on the strength of ongoing team preparedness. Every day. Every fire. Every time.

Practicing how to respond during high-stress periods gave them a reassuring sense of order and control in the middle of chaos. Since no one knew when the next alarm might sound, they worked to be ready *all* the time. Even after a crisis.

All hands reported to the hose tower and wash rack to clean and dry all of the dirty, wet, and still-frozen fire hose that was used on the big blaze. The cotton hose needed to be cleaned and hung to dry to keep it from rotting and mildewing.

After being scrubbed and rinsed, each heavy, fifty-foot length was lifted by hand and hung in the tall, heated hose tower to air out and drip dry. Once it was finally dry, each length was rolled and loaded back onto the hose wagon, ready for the next fire.

In addition to the hose, all of the clothing, and every tool and piece of equipment that had been used on the fire needed to be cleaned and checked for any necessary repairs or replacements—a never-ending but essential job at the fire house. Only after all of the equipment and fire rigs were ready for the next fire could the men begin to slow their pace and return to a more basic routine.

Now almost twenty-five, Big Nick enjoyed a real sense of accomplishment and purpose in his career. He had always wanted to be a firefighter, and after six years with the department, he still did. Simply put, Nicklaus Hollyday loved being a Markford Fireman. He was good at it. He came to appreciate the elements of duty, discipline, service, teamwork, routine, and tradition.

Tradition was a time-honored practice in the fire department. But, by December of 1915, our nation had entered the Industrial Revolution, and it would have been impossible not to notice that changes were happening all around the city—changes that would very soon have a big impact on the way things were done in Markford.

New inventions that promised to make life better and easier were popping up everywhere. Households were transformed overnight as washing machines, sewing machines, hot water heaters, and other exciting new products were becoming widely available.

Electricity, gasoline, and other useful discoveries were taking the country by storm. Early motor cars were beginning to replace the much-loved horse. While these amazing new inventions would soon make life easier, more comfortable, and even safer, they were also about to bring permanent changes to some long-held traditions of the Markford Fire Department.

On Friday, a very flashy—and very noisy—fire wagon had come to the department with no horses pulling it. The fire chief and fire board had ordered a new motor fire buggy! It was a big, noisy, smelly, machine with a steering wheel and a loud bell. And it was, simply . . . *amazing.*

The shiny, new fire buggy seemed to be catching the interest of everyone in Markford, and Big Nick and the other firemen were drawn to the new fang-dangled fire wagon like kids to a candy counter.

It was a 1915 Seagrave motorized fire engine with a bright, glossy, apple-red paint job and elaborate gold-leaf lettering and designs. It was exciting just to look at—it had all the visual draw and excitement of a brand-new carnival ride that everyone wants to try!

It wasn't really a fair fight at all. In the new machine-power era, it was easy to see that the motorized fire engine would be declared the clear winner in a battle between tradition—and *innovation*.

Big Nick knew that a new era was definitely upon them. And he knew what it meant. He felt a heavy, heart-wrenching pain as the reality of losing his beloved Major began to sink in. They were partners. Nick was responsible for him.

As Nick thought about the wheels of progress rolling forward—this time without a courageous spirit and the heart of a hero beating in its chest—he had a hard time thinking of his magnificent Major being replaced by a machine. But, he was also somewhat relieved that Major would no longer be exposed to the extreme stresses and many dangers of firefighting.

During his years with the department, Major had courageously led the team, thundering through the narrow, winding streets of Markford pulling the heavy steamer at a full gallop. Certainly not easy to stop, there was always the potential for wrecks and accidents.

Nick had seen way too many of them, and he winced at the thought of Major suffering that kind of devastating injury. Major had given his all—saving lives and protecting property. He had given enough. It was Nick's job to keep him safe. They were partners. He was responsible for him . . . .

Later that day, Chief Henry called Big Nick into his office to discuss Nick's idea of donating the coats from the burned-out factory to the children at the orphanage. The chief told Nick he had talked to the mayor of Markford, and the mayor had talked with the factory owner. The owner said the department could have them—with a big, *"IF."*

IF the department would take care of drying the coats, taking them to the orphanage, and passing them out to the children, they could have *all* of them, just in time for Christmas! Nick was thrilled, and the chief congratulated him on the great idea that would make a real difference to the kids at the orphanage.

The chief also talked with Nick about the big changes that were coming to the Markford Fire Department. Very soon, the new motor-driven Seagrave fire engine would be replacing Steamer #1, Hose Wagon #1, and five fire horses. Nick was given the assignment to arrange the switch-over from horse-drawn wagons to motor-driven fire trucks.

Within a couple of minutes, Big Nick's schedule had gone from, "busy as usual," to, "busier than ever!" With the orphanage coat project and the fire engine project, Nick was suddenly going to have a couple of weeks that were overflowing with activities and responsibilities.

Even though he knew it was a lot to get accomplished, he had a good feeling knowing that the chief felt he could count on him. Nick set to work, developing a plan to pick up and deliver all the winter coats before he ran out of time.

The next day was Saturday, and Nick would finally have the day off with May—it was her day off, too, just what they needed! As Nick made his way up the neatly shoveled front walk, he could already smell . . . the . . . *cinnamon!*

He smiled from ear-to-ear, knowing what it meant—and could hardly wait for a slice of the best pie in the county. May's apple-cinnamon pie had their little brown house smelling better than a bakery!

As he opened the door, May happily threw herself into Nick's open arms, and told him, "I have a surprise for you!" Thinking he had already figured it out, Nick said, "What do you mean, a *surprise?* I already smelled it! It's apple-cinnamon pie!"

May said, "It's not *just* pie, silly. Come look!"

As Nick entered the living room, it was glowing with candlelight. He saw that May had written the words, *"Pine Glen"* on a piece of paper, and set it on the mantle. She had spread a blanket on the floor in front of the fireplace, and set up a winter picnic in front of the warm fire.

"I couldn't wait for the snow to melt at Pine Glen, so I brought Pine Glen *here!* It's almost your birthday, so it's an early-birthday winter picnic!"

Nick asked, "Can we have pie first?"

As Nick savored the delicious apple-cinnamon pie, May began to dish up their lunch. At the exact same moment, they both said, "I have *so* much to tell you." They both laughed, and then Nick said, with his mouth full, "You go first." May looked at him smiling, and said, "Are you *sure?*"

Big Nick was looking down at his plate, scraping the sweet, gooey-good cinnamon sauce and buttery flakes of pastry into one last bite. Enjoying the last bits on his fork, which was still in his mouth, he said, "Mmm hmmm! You go first!"

"Alright . . . ," said May. She reached for a small box that was packed in with the picnic, wrapped in plain, brown paper and tied with simple white string. Handing it to Nick, May said, "Open this."

Confused, Nick looked at May and said, "I thought you had something to *tell* me."

"OPEN IT!" said May.

Nick took his fork out of his mouth, and set it on the plate in his lap. He untied the string . . . unwrapped the box . . . and slowly lifted the lid. His eyebrows pulled together as he tried to make sense of what it was.

He reached in and pulled out a pair of tiny, white, crocheted baby booties. There were little pink and blue rosebuds embroidered on the toes, and around each ankle was a new, white satin ribbon tied into a perfect, crisp bow. Still pinching the tiny booties between his thumb and forefinger, Nick reached for May, toppling his plate from his lap, and sending parts of the picnic scattering.

Like he was making an announcement that May hadn't heard, Nick grabbed her gently by both shoulders and said loudly, "May! You're gonna have a *baby!*" Laughing out loud, May said with delight, *"You're* gonna be a *daddy!"*

At that moment, nothing else mattered to Nick. Already feeling protective of May and their unborn baby, he held her to his chest in the kind of loving hug that's meant to last a lifetime. He had never loved her more. And yet, right then—right at that moment as he held her—his love grew to love them both.

Nick had been looking forward to having a family with May for a long time. The two were now chuckling as they straightened out the picnic. "I wonder if it's a boy or a girl," Nick pondered aloud, as he took a bite of his ham sandwich, and marveled at the impossibly tiny booties.

They started to mention both boy names and girl names as they popped into their heads. May stopped chewing her bite of sandwich and went wide-eyed when Nick started smiling and said, "Maybe it'll be *twins!"*

As they finished their early-birthday winter picnic, they talked about their hopes and dreams for their new baby. Nick was filled with boastful pride—and overwhelming gratitude—knowing that their Hollyday baby already had a last name. And a warm home. And a loving family to call its own.

Later that day, Nick told May about the huge changes coming to the fire department, and that Major would soon be replaced by the Seagrave. He was very concerned about Major, and what changes would be in store for him. Nick explained to May that he hoped to be able to purchase Major when the fire department retired him.

Nick also told May that the chief had given him the big job of getting the coats from the burned-out factory, drying them, and delivering them to the orphanage for Christmas—which was only two weeks away! This was going to be a huge undertaking with everything else that was going on, and a lot needed to be done in a very short time. Nick would really need some help.

May immediately offered to help out with the coat project. Nick answered, protectively, "No, May . . . now, I don't want you working too hard." May took a fast swipe at Nick with the dish towel, and Nick pretended he needed to protect himself.

"Don't be ridiculous!" she said, continuing to dry a plate from the picnic. "I'll ask Emmy and our friends. I know they'd *love* to help!"

Nick said, "I'm pretty sure I can get some of the guys to help with taking the coats to the orphanage. And I'm *pretty sure* they'd love to help . . . ."

The Christmas coat plan was coming together!

The next day was Sunday. Nick reported back to work only to hear that the very next week the new Seagrave would be back in the station, and they would all need to learn how to use it. Able to pump 750 gallons of water a minute and carry its own hose, this new fire engine was quite a piece of modern engineering!

Since every fireman would need to know everything about the new fire engine and be fully trained on how to properly use it, it would still be about a month before the Seagrave could be put into full, active service.

And since the new engine would replace five horses—gasoline instead of straw and hay would have to be stored somewhere—the horse stalls would have to come down to make room.

It was hard to believe that very soon, the magnificent fire horses would all be gone—and fire house would be overpowered by the smell of gasoline and oil.

A form of life that had given love, work, devotion, and the desire to please everyone would be stepping into history for all time—with only the wonderful stories, heroic tales, and cherished memories of the horses who had given firefighting their all, remaining.

12
The Bad Fire

While everyone was coming to grips with the many changes that were heading their way, another fire happened that was a real game-changer. A huge, terrible fire changed *everything* for the Markford Fire Department.

At least once or twice a year, the north winds would come to town. Known as "Northers," this weather pattern brought strong, dry winds that worried everyone. The Markford firemen knew that the fierce winds actually fanned the fire with extra oxygen, causing it to burn even hotter and the flames to spread more quickly.

Fire occurring on a windy day was nothing to look forward to. And this was one of those days. Early Monday morning, a strong north wind was steadily blowing. Nick was calmly grooming Major when the stunning explosion hit . . . .

BOOM!

The fire house was literally rocked by a thunderous explosion that happened just five blocks south of the fire house! Every living thing flinched as a natural reaction to the unexpected, violent impact of the blast.

All of the department's south-side upstairs windows were blown in! Sharp fragments of broken glass were launched inward, filling the upstairs with flying, jagged shards. Luckily, no one was upstairs at the time, and no firemen were hurt.

An enormous inside explosion had triggered a blaze within Markford's largest cabinet and fine-furniture factory! The building was literally filled with wood products, shavings, and sawdust.

To make matters worse, many rooms of the factory were used for finishing the cabinets and furniture, and they were filled with highly flammable solvents, chemicals, paints, stains, and varnish!

Just as they knew that fire and wind were a dangerous combination, every firefighter also knew that fire, wind, and highly flammable elements were a downright *deadly combination.*

Chief Henry immediately set off the station alarm and ran outside. He was greeted by a large, cauliflower-shaped cloud of black, dirty, smoke with debris falling from the sky, just blocks away from the fire house! Blaze was yipping and barking excitedly, clearly startled and somewhat disoriented by the loud explosion. Nick tried to calm her quickly with a reassuring pat.

Everyone in the fire house already knew . . . this was another big one. Hopefully, they would be able to handle it without too much difficulty, but the *wind . . . .*

As the gonging alarm was sounding, the horses were all anxiously prancing, stomping, and in a hurry to get to their respective stations. They were released, and they stepped right up to their wagons. Their harnesses dropped, and were immediately hooked. Once they were set, the firemen jumped on board, and were ready to head out as fast as they could.

Just as the chief started to roll out of the fire house, ***KABOOM!***

A second, jolting explosion occurred, again filling the sky with even heavier plumes of black smoke and falling debris! The huge explosion could be heard by everyone in Markford, as the building was right in the center of the industrial district!

Many folks from Markford were employed at the cabinet factory, and quite a few workers were hurt in the blast.

The tower of smoke ahead of the firemen was billowing jet-black, and moving very rapidly to the south. They could clearly see the leaping flames spiraling high into the already-smoky morning sky! As Blaze and all the wagons left the fire house, it was total chaos. Masses of townspeople and all of their horses and wagons were trying to head toward the fire!

The chief had a very tough time navigating safely through the congested roadway. The streets were terribly overcrowded with many people, automobiles, streetcar trolleys, horses, and horse-drawn rigs. The thunderous explosions that shook the buildings and the earth had frightened many horses that were now rearing and bolting out of control, and mobs of concerned folks were running to see what had happened, and racing to help the injured!

All of the confusion and throngs of people in the packed streets made it difficult and dangerous for the firemen and the fire horses. With bells clanging and Blaze barking wildly, the chief and his crew finally made it through the crowd, and arrived at the monstrous fire.

Chief Henry had been in the cabinet factory many times for inspections, and he knew all about the numerous hazards inside. Knowing it contained all the elements of a ferociously hot fire had him concerned right out of the gates. This was a big one that could rapidly grow to an out-of-control blaze. He knew immediately that this fire would require extra help and resources.

He sent a second- and third-alarm runner to ring the town bell for many more resources and the critically needed manpower this firefight would demand.

Upon his arrival, the chief found just what he expected: a large, fast-moving blaze, fed by all the combustible components from the cabinet factory—and there would be no relief from the wind. Smoke blocked any view of the building. Damage was severe and many people were racing from the structure. Folks were in the lot next to the fire helping those who were hurt or burned. Many horses were loose and wildly galloping about with their wagons uncontrolled.

The block-long, two-story, brick-and-wood factory building was well-involved with fire. The center of the big structure had already collapsed from the explosions, and the wind was pushing the fire to the south, toward many other exposures and buildings!

Fire service training and experience prepares firemen for such events. It teaches them what to do, what to look for, and how to plan and react to emergencies such as this. The fire chief was right at home in this chaotic environment, and fully able to handle all of the important the issues.

As he carefully planned his attack on the fire, he would ensure the crews followed the five basic rules that were set in this prioritized order:

Markford Fire Department
- *Rescue*
- *Exposures*
- *Confinement*
- *Extinguishment*
- *Mop-up*

The chief shouted out commands through his speaking horn, but it seemed his trained and experienced firemen already knew exactly what to do and how to do it.

Nick, Dave, Major, Ben, and Bob pulled Steamer #1 right up to edge of the Connecticut River to secure a good water supply.

Big Nick gave his familiar command: **"Hold, Major!"** Major set his powerful hooves and stopped the wagon like a dart hitting the board. The mighty steamer was set firmly in place.

Hose Wagon #1 was positioned right next to the steamer to lay a hose line to the fire.

Nick and Dave hooked up the big suction hoses to the pump, and then hooked up the discharge hose as Hose Wagon #1 started off toward the fire, laying its hose along the ground as it drove away.

The hook-and-ladder wagon stopped at the fire's exposure side, preparing to wet it down with water from a master stream.

The ladder team set their ladders and climbed up the uninvolved portion of the structure, not knowing if there might be another blast. They cautiously made their way to the front office as fast as they could, prepared to rescue anyone who might still be inside, needing help to get out.

Dave opened the throttle and the big steamer shuddered to life like a roaring, metallic, fire-breathing dragon with a job to do—smoke and fire belching from its boiler stack.

Big Nick unhooked the team of wide-eyed horses and, with excited Blaze running alongside, took the team to a safe area behind another building, tying them securely. Remembering from the last fire, Nick quickly covered them with their heavy, warm blankets, and gave each horse and Blaze a reassuring pat before returning to help fight the huge fire.

The cold, north wind kept blowing, sometimes with gusts of thirty or forty miles per hour! The fierce winds were pushing the flames further to the south, drying and heating all of the exposed wooden structures down-wind. Smoke and fiery sparks were flying through the air and dropping down on wooden roofs to the south of the fire.

The chief sent the wagon crews that responded to the second alarm to help fight the main fire. The crews that responded to the third alarm were sent to help contain and control the fires that were starting on the rooftops south of the main fire.

He also assigned the two chemical wagons to patrol the area, checking for any smoke or fire anywhere south of the main fire. Even with the extra wagon crews, the chief knew he did not have enough manpower to handle such an extensive emergency.

Most cities in early America had rules that required able-bodied men to help the fire department in emergencies. They had to follow the instructions of local fire marshals or fire officers at all times. Arrests could actually be made if anyone refused.

The chief knew he would have to rely on help from the men of Markford on this big one. He instructed his firemen to seek assistance from any men who could help to suppress the fires that were started by the many wind-blown sparks and flying embers.

The terrible inferno was continuing to rage completely out of control, but thanks to the Connecticut River, there was enough water—and enough pumping steam engines—to continue fighting the "red devil," — *fire!*

Mercifully, the wind finally started to calm. By early evening, after ten hours battling the blaze with help from the men in the community, most of the smaller fires had been put out or controlled.

The big main fire, however, still raged with great intensity. Leaping flames, choking smoke, and boiling fire was everywhere! It was apparent that the whole factory structure would be entirely lost!

By now, Markford Fire Department had almost every piece of its equipment and every fireman attacking this fire. The ground around the fire zone was strewn with miles of fire hose that had been reeled out, making the whole area look like a giant, tangled snake's nest. A call-back of every off-duty fireman was started.

The mayor arrived, and both he and Chief Henry were very worried about the condition of the building and the terrible danger that existed for the firemen. The building was burning fiercely, and large sections were beginning to fall. Crumbling brick walls, collapsing roof, and curtains of ferocious flames created many hazards for the firemen.

Just as the wind and the fire seemed to calm down for a moment, the "new guy" from headquarters, young Aaron McConnell, offered an optimistic rally cry as he hollered out to his crewmates, ***"I think we're getting the upper hand on this one, boys!"***

When, *KA-THOOONG!*

Another dreadful, explosion with a deep, powerful concussion rocked the south end of the building right where many firemen were working to extinguish the last of the fire! It was an inside explosion that blew a heavy brick, concrete, and timber wall outward like a huge mortar blast onto two hose teams of firemen.

Airborne rubble rained down hard. A rush of dusty smoke and debris-filled air blasted the area like an abrasive sandstorm. Dense, black, cinder-ash swirled heavily, choking and blinding everyone who charged in to help the trapped firemen.

One by one, the wounded firefighters were coming out of the rubble. Some were able to free themselves and made it out of the wreckage on their own. Others were dug out of the deep debris. Although they were all bruised, bloodied, or badly injured, all of them were rescued.

All but one! McConnell had taken a direct hit from the explosion. He was down and still buried!

With the fire still raging, Chief Henry reorganized the grave situation. He immediately put a district chief in charge of rescuing the young fireman who was trapped under an enormous pile of bricks and heavy timbers.

Within the hour, the terribly sad news made its way around the fire zone like a telegraph—McConnell had died in the blast. The new guy from headquarters' Hook and Ladder #1 would fight fires no more.

It was going to be a long, very cold, and incredibly sad night for Nick, Major, and the Markford Fire Department. They stayed through the night to finish hours of work hosing down this awful fire to ensure no embers could reignite.

With dawn approaching, the atmosphere felt like a fast spoon through thin soup; everyone was stirred-up and unsettled. Nick hated that feeling.

They continued to do what they were committed to do—they went on fighting the fire, trying to perform their duties while putting aside the shocking reality of their tragic loss. By the time the fire was contained, the men were well beyond wet and cold. They were exhausted. They were emotionally drained. One of their brothers was gone. They had lost one of their own.

The once-fine cabinet factory was reduced to nothing more than scattered piles of smoking rubble covered with thick, abstract mounds of ice in the formerly bustling industrial district. The Markford Fire Department had done its job of containing the fire, and although no additional structures were lost, no one would be celebrating after this fire.

Chief Henry, still in command and very fatigued, started to release the exhausted firefighting forces to their various fire houses for rest. Almost all of Markford's steamers, hose wagons, ladder wagons—and all of its manpower—had been assigned to the fire during the past twenty hours.

Nick and his crew were finally released from the fire to complete their duties at the fire house, and then head home for some rest and recuperation. Even though he was very weary, the moment he arrived at the fire house Nick was quick to get Major cleaned, warmed, and fed—even before he took care of himself.

Nick talked soft and low to Major as he groomed him—he, too, had experienced a lot of stress in a very short time.

Major seemed attuned to the sadness in Nick's voice. His usual bright-eyed expression and happy disposition were gone. Nick wondered just how much Major understood about what had happened. He seemed depressed and listless, and it was clear that Major would need rest and recuperation, too.

After getting Major fed, warmed up, and settled into his stable, Nick started for home to see his sweet May. He arrived just as she was getting ready to leave for the orphanage. She was so glad and relieved to see him, she rushed to greet him!

But the moment May's eyes met Nick's, she saw the strain and exhaustion reflected in her husband's face. She immediately took off her coat and got Nick seated.

He turned his chair from the table, sat on it backwards, and silently looked up at the ceiling. He locked his fingers together, and pulled his forehead back with the palms of his hands. In an anguished voice, Nick finally said, "We lost one, May. We lost Aaron McConnell."

His voice began to break as he told her, "He was a good man, May. He was a husband . . . a father . . . he has *two young children . . . .*" Grief-stricken, his words dwindled off. May hugged her Big Nick.

She held him, and together they wept for the loss of a dedicated young fireman. They wept for his family. They held on to one another. They knew that together—they would hold on.

When Nick said he was too tired to eat, May decided to stay home with him. Nick insisted that she go to the orphanage, telling her, "The kids are counting on you, May. I'm just gonna lay here and try to get some sleep."

May tucked Big Nick in bed; she smoothed his hair and slowly stroked his brow. When she kissed him softly on his forehead, he was already asleep.

May sat quietly and watched Nick sleeping. She couldn't help thinking about the many dangers of firefighting. She couldn't help thinking of her own little family, and wanting Nick to be with her . . . *always.* As she wiped the tears from her eyes, she said a silent prayer for the McConnell's . . . and for *all* firemen . . . .

By the time May arrived at the orphanage, the staff had already heard the news. It seemed all of Markford had heard, and everyone was saddened and sorry for the tragic loss.

Even the children seemed down, and May couldn't help but notice that some of them were coughing. She was sure that the cold, drafty building was beginning to cause sickness, and if it were warmer, most of this suffering could be prevented.

Something had to be done about cold-hearted Mr. Bloomquist's cruel and tight-fisted ways!

13
The Funeral

Final goodbyes are never easy, and when someone dies, it has a special meaning for each of us. But to those in the fire service it's even more special. Knowing you have lost someone who would lay his life on the line for a stranger made it emotional. Knowing you have lost a brother who would lay his life down to save yours . . . made it *personal.*

The firemen were used to spending long days and hours together—it was part of the job. For many, they actually spent more time with their crew than they did with their own family members. They developed strong bonds with each other, and relieved the stress of being away from their families for such long periods of time by joking around, and sharing many of life's issues with one another.

When firemen lost one of their own—a close crew member they had spent so much time with—it was truly like losing a family member. And now, like a big family, the firemen of Markford would support one another, as together, they faced the sad event that even firemen avoided talking about.

The fire service had an official ceremony for tragedies such as on-duty deaths. The funeral service would be very special: formal, respectful, and solemn. The family of the lost fireman would be given first priority—anything they needed would be provided for them. Fire service funerals were managed and conducted by the fire department, and all family wishes were granted without question.

The ceremony would be held by the fire department with a high level of dignity, and all fire personnel would "turn out" for the task of burying one of their own.

All of the department's plans with the new Seagrave fire engine and the Christmas coat project were put on hold until after the fire department, and all of Markford, could prepare to say goodbye to Aaron McConnell with dignity, honor, and respect.

A very special farewell was being planned for a fine young man with much to live for and, following a long-standing and important tradition, the firemen pulled together to help ease the pain for his family, making sure that his wife and two young children were taken care of.

The funeral would take place in two days, on Thursday, December 16th. Big Nick and the steamer team were put in charge of preparing the wagons for the procession. The hose wagon would carry the casket, and the family carriage would carry Aaron's wife, Sarah, her two young children, and Sarah's mother and father.

Cleaned and polished to a great shine, Nick's crew had the wagon and carriage looking just like new. They draped yards and yards of black fabric around each rig, securing gathered sections into swags with large, black satin bows.

Major was chosen to pull the one-horse wagon carrying the casket; Ben and Bob would be pulling the family carriage. All three horses would have polished black hooves, and each would be outfitted with black leather harnesses with bright metal fittings, and tall, black funeral plumes mounted on their heads.

The glass in the fire station's second-story windows had been quickly replaced, and the front windows were all draped with swags of black cloth that would remain in place for a week after the funeral.

Thursday was overcast and cold; fitting weather for the sad mood of the day. Father Sammon conducted the church services with traditional grace. Many of McConnell's friends gave touching tributes of his kindness and courage, and shared wonderful stories that reinforced the many reasons why this young family man would be greatly missed. Many tears flowed—and the emotional sorrows ran deep.

After the chapel service, the fire department personnel carried the casket from the church with dignified protocol. They carefully loaded it onto the wagon draped with black swags and black satin bows. Sadness filled the air as Sarah and her two children boarded their carriage. Nothing was heard but the soft, whimpering cries of a heartbroken young wife who had lost her love, and the father of their two beautiful children.

Following tradition, hundreds of firemen in full dress from all over Connecticut were in place, ready to march on foot behind the family carriage to pay their respects. Behind them were numerous horse-drawn fire wagons—all there to pay tribute to the young fireman who was gone from their fire family far too soon.

Just as Big Nick readied Major to begin the huge procession, a small voice called out, *"Wait!"*

The family carriage door swung open, and Aaron McConnell's four-year-old son jumped from the coach, running straight to the casket wagon. He stood still, looking up at Big Nick sitting in his full parade dress uniform. Nick looked down at the small boy, whose nose and cheeks were red from the cold.

In silence, Nick lowered his powerful arm and hand for the young boy to hold onto, and in one, effortless motion, he lifted the boy aboard the casket wagon.

The little boy sat next to Nick. Big Nick waited steadfastly as the boy turned backward, peering over his fists as he held onto the back of the wagon's seat. The boy looked first down the length of the casket. And then, down the long procession of firemen in their formal uniforms . . . and the horses . . . and the wagons . . . and more firemen.

He finally turned around, looked up at Big Nick, and said matter-of-factly in his childish voice, "I'm Christopher. You're carrying my Daddy in the parade today." Big Nick clenched and released his jaw, and after a short pause, responded.

"And you. Today I am carrying your daddy—and you."

Big Nick turned and looked at the coachman. He pointed at something, and quickly gave an affirmative nod. The coachman passed McConnell's damaged helmet forward.

Nick gently placed the large, leather helmet on the boy's small head. "Yeah," said Christopher, nodding at Nick and sending the helmet down over his eyes. "Me and my Daddy."

The boy re-adjusted the heavy, battered helmet that smelled of smoke and the sweat of his father. Looking forward now, he was ready for the parade to begin. Nick continued to work his jaw, trying to command his tears not to fall.

Before Nick could give the forward command, Major seemed to understand the significance of the moment. He lowered his head and planted his massive front hoof down with such authority that it sent forward a fan of white snow spray.

He then lifted his massive head decorated with the tall, black, ostrich feather plume, and gracefully arched his neck. With a powerful show of dignified character, Major filled the cold, winter air with two perfect vapor trails as he exhaled mightily. He was ready. He had an important job to accomplish. And he seemed to know it . . . .

Watching him, Nick recognized a strength in Major's spirit that helped bolster his own. Nick took a slow, deep, breath, and as he exhaled, he sat tall with the respectful posture that the occasion called for.

A fallen brother's son was waiting. And watching.

And Big Nick had an important job to do. He was ready. With Nick's gentle command, Major stepped off smoothly toward the cemetery with his head held high.

The clopping of Major's black, polished hooves echoed against the brick-paved street, with long interruptions of quiet as they passed through patches of snow. As Major led the parade carrying Christopher and his daddy, one soft bell rang in the background: *ding . . . ding . . . ding . . . ding . . . ding . . .*

The firemen—all in full dress uniform—marched slowly and reverently to the cadence of the bell. In a statement of unity, they marched in formation—every stride in step with the others.

They tried to look straight ahead as a show of honor and respect, but many lowered their heads to wipe away tears that fell as they thought about the brother they had lost . . . about the heartbreaking image of a little boy wearing his father's big helmet . . . and about all of the things that were important in their own lives.

The solemn procession continued down Oak Street, with proud Major leading, and Big Nick seated by young Christopher. There were so many Markford citizens standing along the sidewalk to acknowledge their gratitude and pay their respects, that they spilled over into the streets. Many of them were wiping their tears, too.

The graveside service was short and respectful. Father Sammon gave a wonderful prayer and blessing to the family and to all in attendance, ending with the reassuring message of God's eternal love, and telling the fireman's family, "Today, this good man—Aaron McConnell—is heaven-bound, and his homecoming will be sweet."

The cold, December skies pulled together and formed a cloud cover that began to darken the afternoon earlier than usual. It almost seemed that the heavens knew how the people of Markford were feeling, and the weather provided the perfect, ending tribute to such a solemn and emotional day.

14
A Great Christmas is Coming

Two days after the funeral, Nick was off-duty and home with May. Things just didn't seem right. Life was not back in order yet, and Nick hated that unsettled feeling.

There were lots of heavy hearts in Markford: in addition to the funeral, there were many who were injured or out of a job with the loss of the coat factory *and* the cabinet factory. Christmas was approaching very quickly, and it seemed there was just too much to get accomplished—and too little time.

Nick thought about all that still needed to be done. He thought about the coat project for the children at the orphanage; the new Seagrave fire engine project; and the responsibility that he and the other firemen would have regularly checking on the McConnell family. But even with all of these important jobs to be completed, none of them was as important to Big Nick as May, and the baby he already loved growing within her.

One week before Christmas, on December 19th, Nick and Dave were making their plan for the Christmas coat project. True to their word, they were ready to spearhead the project. Together, they went to pick up the large load from the coat factory. The weather was getting colder and colder. Much more wintery than Nick ever remembered. The wind seemed more powerful, the cold seemed more frigid, and the day was more overcast—no sun at all.

Well over one hundred good-quality blue coats and brown jackets were recovered from the undamaged part of the burned-out factory. Although all of them were salvageable, most of them were wet and frozen, and many still smelled of smoke. Nick and Dave loaded them into the department's horse van, and together, they took the enormous mound of cold, wet, wool and buttons to the fire house.

The coats were more important now than ever—donations to the fire department had dwindled in December. With two major fires happening so close together, there were lots of folks and families in Markford who were in need of generous donations. This year, many would be counting on the kindness of their churches, friends, and neighbors.

May and her friends sorted through the few coats that were already dry and in good shape—folding them and setting them aside. They washed and rinsed out the rest that were wet and smelled of smoke. When the ladies had finished, it would be up to Nick and Dave to get the coats dry.

Dave came up with an ingenious solution for drying such a large number of coats. He rigged a chain that would be raised to the top of the hose tower, and he would attach the coats onto the chain as Nick pulled it up.

He sent a length of wire through the hanging loop that was sewn into the back collar of each coat. With a simple twist of the wire through a link of chain, each coat was securely attached. Very quickly, the chain was filled from top to bottom with coats in every size imaginable! From floor to ceiling, a soaring column of navy blue and brown wool began to drip-dry in the heated hose tower.

Back at the orphanage, the children hurried to May like chicks to a hen when she returned. She had been spending time at the hospital because of the many injuries from the factory fires.

It broke her heart to see that, in addition to the raggedy coats they wore inside, many of the children now covered their hands with holey mittens and woolen socks to keep warm. This year, it was colder outside. It was colder *inside,* too.

May told Nick of the difficult, wintery conditions for the children. They were cold. They were suffering. She was afraid that many were starting to get sick. And it seemed that for most of them, hoping for any Christmas at all was a waste of time and energy that they just couldn't afford. Sometimes, nothing is more costly than having the warm glow of hope squashed by cold disappointment.

After Old Spike had retired, Mr. Bloomquist said that hiring a new maintenance man was, "Definitely, not in the budget!" But actually, someone *had* come by to fill Spike's vacancy. After spending just ten minutes with Mr. Bloomquist, however, the handyman told him, "You know . . . you are one bitter, little piece of work!"

He packed up his tools, and that was the end of it. No other maintenance man was given a try. Even now, years later, the orphanage *still* didn't have a maintenance man. The building and furnishings were still falling apart. The paint was still peeling. The heater still wasn't working. And Mr. Bloomquist, *well*, he was still . . . *Mr. Bloomquist.*

Nick and May talked about what could be done. Without their help, it seemed nothing would change. Ever since Spike had retired, some of the orphanage's traditions had dried up and disappeared—it seemed they had been retired, too.

There hadn't been a Christmas tree in the great hall for several years now. Maybe now was the right time to renew some traditions!

And maybe . . . *just maybe* . . . there was a way to make the wish for a warm and happy Christmas celebration really come true!

Monday brought another cold, wintery day to Markford. Nick was back to work and, as usual, he started grooming Major early in the morning. The grooming and brushing ritual was very calming to both Nick and Major. Checking his feet and hooves, feeding him, cleaning out the stall, putting down fresh straw, and pouring clean water in his drinking well—they were all a part of Nick and Major's morning routine. And every day, Nick also brushed and fed Blaze, ensuring Major's faithful companion was well taken care of, too.

After finishing, Nick went to check on the coats that he and Dave had hung in the hose tower. He was pleasantly surprised to find them all drying quite well—despite the cold weather! He couldn't help feeling pleased with how good they looked. In fact, if he hadn't known they were salvaged from the belly of the burned-out coat factory, he would never have guessed that each of these "new" coats already had a fiery past!

He squeezed a few sleeves and collars, checking for dampness. Nick turned up the thermostat on the old oil-fired stove from "medium" to "high," to help the coats dry more quickly. The old heating stove got him thinking about the heater at the orphanage—and how it needed repairing. He made some decisions about how to handle fixing it.

At lunch time, Nick shared with Chief Henry and the other firemen what May had told him about the very hard times for the children at the orphanage. The chief sat there, quietly shaking his head as he ate the warm, delicious, beef stew Dave had prepared for the fire house crew.

As they were getting off-duty, Nick and Dave went to the chief to ask for permission to take Major and the old feed wagon out to cut a Christmas tree for the orphanage. After hearing the stories Nick told at lunch, not only did the chief approve, but wanted to help them get the tree! They would head out together in the morning.

The Tuesday morning sun was trying hard to burn through the freezing, misty fog. As he prepared to leave the warm and tidy little brown house, Nick held May with her back to his chest, rocking her back and forth under his chin, his arms reaching around her tummy. Nick asked May, "So, I'll see you later today at the orphanage, right?"

Still wrapped in the rocking hug, May's face lit up with excitement as she thought about the good things that were coming for the children. She smiled, and said, *"Right!"* And she assured him, "We'll be ready!"

May turned, and pulled Nick's coat collar up around his knitted scarf to protect him from the bitter cold, and just before he closed the door . . . he winked at her!

As Nick, Dave, and the chief finished tying the familiar chair securely in the wagon, they loaded up the axe and the saw, and drove Major straight to Spike and Emmy's. With Spike all bundled up and seated in his designated chair—puffing on his pipe—Nick tucked the cozy blanket snugly around him and said, "All right now, Spike. You keep a look out for a good one!"

Spike chuckled as the four of them headed off into the woods to find just the right tree. And when he found it, Spike took the pipe out of his mouth, using it to point with, and said, "Mmm hmmm . . . that's the one . . . right there!"

The men set to work, cutting down the beautiful twelve-foot spruce. They loaded the evergreen beauty onto the feed wagon, and with Nick's low, *"Git up, Major,"* off they all went to the orphanage. As Major was prancing down the roadway with the finely formed Christmas tree, Old Spike and his pipe sent faint little puffer clouds of smoke skyward.

Along the way, Nick told Chief Henry, "You know, chief, the orphanage is going to look different from how you might remember it. The whole building is starting to fall into disrepair." As Nick told him about the paint beginning to peel, the strict food limitations, and almost no medical supplies, Chief Henry looked down, shaking his head in sad disbelief.

And, when Nick mentioned the broken heater and said that the children were wearing their coats indoors and covering their hands with wool socks to keep warm, the chief had had enough. He said he planned to talk to the mayor, who would help make sure some changes would be coming to the Markford Children's Orphanage that would last long after Christmas!

Arriving at the orphanage at one o'clock, the men secretly unloaded the tall, stately spruce tree while the children were still in class. It took all three of them to carry it in and set it up in the massive—but cold—great hall.

Nick sawed off the wide, full, bottom boughs to reveal enough of the trunk for the tree to be settled into a huge tub and surrounded by heavy bricks to secure it and keep it upright. Buckets of water were added to help keep it fresh.

May kept her promise. They *were* ready! With the afternoon classes and child care covered by novice sisters, May, Emmy, Sister Michelle Marie, Sister Barbara Elizabeth, and Cooky set to work; decorating the massive evergreen with the ornaments, tinsel, garlands, and a bundle of holly trimmings they had all chipped in to buy.

While the ladies decorated the tree, Nick, Dave, and the chief went down to the basement to check on the old steam heater. They found exactly what they had expected; due to a lack of maintenance, the heater was not working correctly. With a little care and a fairly simple repair, the heater could be fixed in time to provide a warm Christmas for the children.

The three men headed back to the fire house; Dave still had time to talk to a plumber from the city.

After some discussion, it was decided that the sisters would handle the ladder-climbing to top-off the tree. Spike tried not to laugh as the two women wrestled their habits *and* the ladder. But, like a small volcano, his tight-lipped trumpet-sputter erupted into a belly laugh as Sister Michelle Marie cautiously mounted the wobbly wooden contraption!

Sister Barbara Elizabeth held the ladder as Sister Michelle Marie climbed up . . . and up . . . and *reached* out as far as she possibly could to finally place the star on the top of the tree! When they all cheered her accomplishment, the celebration startled the sister, and sent her whooping and swaying as she grabbed for the ladder—shaking unsteadily—and still whooping as Sister Barbara Elizabeth helped her regain her balance!

The adorned Christmas tree was amazingly beautiful! Shiny glass balls shone like round, tinted mirrors suspended from the sweeping boughs. Colorful glass-bead garlands draped their way round and round the evergreen, and long, silvery tinsel twinkled and trickled down from every branch, mimicking nature's glittering winter icicles.

Small bunches of holly were tucked into the boughs, making it look as though the evergreen was abloom with green-and-red winter-blossoms! The gold star on top was the perfect, glistening grand finale. Even Old Spike agreed it was the finest Christmas tree he had ever seen!

Spike helped the ladies by snipping the extra pine boughs and holly trimmings into smaller pieces, and May and Emmy worked together to wire the fresh greens into a colossal wreath. They attached a long piece of ruby-red velvet that Emmy tied into a big, plush, bow. May even stitched real jingle bells onto the bow's flowing, red streamers!

It had been a long day for Old Spike, and it was time for him to be, "gittin' on home." May put on her long, black-wool coat, and pulled her black hat down as far as she could to protect her ears. As she waited for Spike and Emmy to bundle up in their winter woolens, she hung the handsome wreath on the front door by latching the bent-wire hook on the back over the door ring.

On their way out, the three of them stood back and smiled with satisfaction at their finished holiday handiwork. Still smiling, May looked over her shoulder to watch Spike and Emmy's jolly laughter as she gave the red velvet bow a little wiggle, sending the bells jingling. She pinched off a small piece of holly from the wreath, and tucked it festively into the side of her hat.

May made it back from Spike and Emmy's just in time for the afternoon classes to be released. Usually, there were chores to be done and homework to finish before supper. But when classes were excused *this* Tuesday afternoon, all items on the "to do" list were erased as the children were greeted by the glorious Christmas tree in the great hall!

The whole staff gathered in the big, chilly room, overcome with joy as they watched the children's faces light up with happy excitement! The children rushed to gather around the spectacular tree, gasping, pointing, and laughing out loud . . . wide-eyed in joyful amazement at the beautiful, breathtaking surprise!

Their loud, merry squeals and shouts of happy delight were offset by a different kind of noise . . . the oddly muffled sound of over sixty children—standing in the great hall wearing coats and hats—clapping with wool socks and holey mittens on their hands.

Yes, the spirit of Christmas could be felt throughout the orphanage, despite Mr. Bloomquist! And speaking of Mr. Bloomquist, even with all of the loud disruption and noise, he and his walking stick were nowhere to be seen.

After supper, Cooky and May dashed out to the play yard and pulled the two snow-covered, rickety wooden wagons to the back delivery porch. They quickly swept the snow off as best they could, then pulled them in, and parked them near the hot stove. Cooky kept the long-handled string mop close by to handle the melting snow!

By Wednesday morning, Nick was back at the department, working hard to figure out and memorize the operational manuals for the Seagrave. When he took a break, he and his crew harnessed Major to the feed wagon and went to check on the McConnell family, delivering three boxes of food to Sarah and the children.

While they were there, Nick invited all of them to the Christmas celebration they had planned for Saturday morning. "If we can make it," answered Sarah, without much enthusiasm. Offering her the support she needed, Nick reassured Sarah by saying, "We'll make sure you can."

By Thursday, all of the coats were finally dry! Every last coat. From the very biggest down to the smallest of the small. Nick and Dave began untwisting each wire, releasing the coats, one-by-one, from Dave's drying device. Each was given a good, hard shake, a simple fold in half, and then added to the growing stack of navy blue coats and brown jackets.

While Nick was on duty at the fire department, May spent Thursday night at home with her brown, furry shoulder wrap with pompoms on the ties, a large scrap of ruby-red velvet, her sewing bag and scissors, and the pinch of holly from her hat. She went straight to work; her nimble fingers transforming the ordinary into nothing short of magical. Tomorrow was Big Nick's birthday!

Friday was Christmas Eve morning. At eight o'clock, Dave arrived at the orphanage with the Markford city plumber. After a quick check, the plumber gave Dave the *good* news. "We're lucky—this will be an easy repair!" As he replaced a valve and cleaned the soot from the venting flue, the plumber told Dave the *bad* news—a winter snowstorm was headed their way.

Like most folks in Markford, he had planned to spend time with his family, and they needed to get on the road if they were going to beat the snow flurries. Dave shook the plumber's hand, and thanked him more than once for taking time away from his family plans to repair the furnace for the children before Christmas!

The furnace was turned on. It hissed and clunked loudly . . . then it whistled off a long, high-pitched whine . . . and threw in some serious knocks and pings as it came to life. Slow and steady, it began sending heat throughout the building so thoroughly pleasing, it was like a heartbeat pumping hot pudding!

By Friday afternoon, the chief and the firemen were developing a plan to deliver their Christmas surprise in a way that no one in Markford had ever seen before! It was "all hands on deck" at the fire house as the plan was finalized.

Their idea was to load up the new Seagrave (as it would not go into active service for another month) with the toys and new coats, and drive to the orphanage in Markford's first motorized fire engine! They would then have their celebration next to the splendid tree in the great hall.

Anyone who was available was helping prepare for the big Saturday morning Christmas celebration. The firemen were loading the mounds of coats, which had been separated and bundled by size, into the hose bed of the Seagrave.

May and the other ladies divided the toys into groups for babies, youngsters, and adolescents. They wrapped and secured the extra food items they had made. When it was all ready, everything was loaded onto the Seagrave.

As the group was finishing their task in the late afternoon, it was easy to see by the size of their smiles that they understood the difference between *hard work* . . . and *heart work.* It seemed that out of the joy and love of doing for others, the more they gave, the more they had to give.

Christmas Eve was cold and quiet outside. But the work going on *inside* made the fire house the most heartwarming place to be in all of Markford. Major and Blaze watched all the excitement and activity from Major's stall, both of them comfy and snug in thick, sweet straw.

Nick would be spending the night at the department, and he was concerned about May spending the night at home alone with the snowstorm coming. May assured him that she would be happy to stay at the orphanage—now that it was *warm!*

Nick drove May to the orphanage and quietly walked her inside. It was eight o'clock. The children were all in bed. May couldn't wait for Nick to see the tree, now decorated with such splendor!

Nick's face lit up when he saw it! He nodded excitedly at May, and silently mouthed the words, *"It's beautiful!"* They held one another, smiling as they gazed at the lovely tree. And then, May turned with a jerk.

She whispered, *"Oh! I almost forgot!"* She reached into her purse. As she pulled something out, she continued, still whispering. *"Happy birthday, Nicklaus Hollyday! I didn't have time to wrap it!"*

Nick unrolled a pointed, ruby-red velvet hat with furry trim, a fur pompom at the point, and a piece of holly pinned on one side. He smiled wide, and didn't have to be asked to try it on!

As he pulled the hat onto his head, May covered her laugh with her hand. She said, quietly, *"Maybe I should call you, Saint Nicklaus Hollyday!"* They both laughed as quietly as they could, and Nick gave May a hug and a quick kiss goodbye at the door.

With the children in bed, Cooky was in the kitchen humming Christmas carols, and magically transforming sugar, butter, flour, spices, and bulging mounds of rising yeast dough into small mountains of sticky-sweet soft cinnamon rolls, cookies, and other delectable baked delights.

May gathered the sisters, and pulled the wooden wagons carrying newspapers, a pair of scissors, and a ball of string to one of the long dining tables. May prepared to show them how to make the paper cones she had learned to make from her mother when she was just a child.

Setting the stack of papers on the table, May promised, "It's *so easy!* I've been making these since I was little. We used to carry things in them all the time!"

Separating out a large, double page, May began to teach the teachers. With their own pages of newspaper ready, the curious sisters followed along, step by step:

"First, you fold a page of newspaper in half, diagonally. Into a triangle . . . like this." May smoothed the diagonal crease with her fingers, making a large triangle.

"Keep the point at the top, and then roll the corner point on your left all the way around and in till it meets the top point, like this." She rolled the left corner around and in until it met the tall point of the triangle.

"When the points meet, pinch them together," said May, pinching the pointed corners together. The cone was already taking shape.

"Then, you bring the last corner point on the right all the way around the outside. Meet it up with the other points . . . and pinch it in with them, like this." She rolled the last corner around the outside of the cone, lining it up with the other corner points, and held all three points together in a firm pinch.

"Then you twist all the corners together tight, so you can set it down, like this." May pinched and twisted the tops of the corner points around firmly—until they were wound into a tight twist that could hold itself together; then she laid her cone on the table, and the sisters followed.

TWIST TOP & BOTTOM TOGETHER

"Now you're ready to tie it off. Cut a piece of string about two feet long, and fold it in half." May looped the cut piece of string in half.

"Keep the string folded in half, and tie it around the twisted paper in a double knot." She tied the double string around the twisted corners, making sure to leave enough of the loop end to make a handle. She tied it again to knot it securely.

MAKE BIG LOOP TO CARRY

TIE TOP & BOTTOM TOGETHER WITH HEAVY STRING

"See? The loop makes the handle!" May lifted up by the string-loop handle, showing the sisters a perfect little paper cone.

"Now you just tie the bottom off with a short piece of string to keep it closed tight." May snipped a twelve-inch piece of string from the ball, and tied a simple double knot around the bottom.

As the sisters completed their first efforts at cone-making, they smiled enthusiastically at their results.

Their smiles fizzled like a flat tire, however, as May then said, "And now, you just have to make twenty-eight more—*each!"*

May chuckled at the looks on their faces, and still chuckling, assured them, "We'll be done before you know it."

Cooky's singing became infectious, and soon, all four of them were joyfully, but quietly, singing Christmas carols—the songs of the season.

FILL WITH
CHRISTMAS
GOODIES

May and the sisters sang and rolled and tied, until eighty-seven paper cones were loaded into the wagons—one for each ward—and one for each of the two McConnell children.

15
Christmas Major

Christmas morning of 1915 arrived! Markford provided a winter backdrop as perfect as a shaken snow globe, and it continued to snow heavily. Over two feet had fallen during the night, and the deep mounds and snowdrifts that had iced over in the dark were now building vertically like glittering, double-scoop vanilla ice cream cones.

Along with the snowflakes, excitement filled the air at the fire house—despite the icy setback! The on-duty firemen were arriving to relieve those going off duty. It was hard to travel in such conditions, but the plan was still on—everyone knew there were a lot of children looking forward to a good Christmas!

After all . . . a little snow never stopped Saint Nick!

At the orphanage, the children were chirping and twittering excitedly like the first birds of spring. The mood was electric. They could *afford* to be energized. They could *afford* to be hopeful. They were finally *warm . . . .*

When May entered the kitchen, she actually gasped! "Ohhh . . . Cooky!" Cooky had her delectable variety of luscious, sugary treats arranged on trays and platters so beautifully—it looked like a fancy French pastry shop! As May admired the dazzling selection of decorated gingerbread men, rich, golden butter cookies, and soft, sticky-sweet cinnamon rolls, Cooky smiled with satisfaction.

May was excited to finish the paper cone project, knowing the portable pockets would soon be filled to overflowing with festive delights! She gathered the novice sisters, and they prepared the assembly line. They set big tubs on the table in the order they would add each item into the cones.

Just as they were about to begin, Mr. Paul and Father Sammon stopped by with a special treat. Three small, wooden crates filled with tangerines! Most of the wards had never seen the exotic little dimple-skinned oranges before, and none of them had ever eaten one! As May thanked the men for their contribution, she was able to talk them into staying—after all, they wouldn't want to miss seeing the excited children, eager to taste the tangerines!

Very quickly, the enthusiastic men were lending a hand with the assembly line. The group loaded the cones in this order: a scoop of peanuts, a tangerine, a few candies, a butter cookie, a gingerbread man, and a candy cane. As each cone was filled with tasty treasure, it was nestled in with the others in the wooden wagons. They loaded sixty-eight cones with *all* the goodies, and nineteen with only gingerbread and butter cookies for the younger children.

At the fire house, everything was set! Dave headed off to pick up the young McConnell family, and Spike and Emmy, as well.

The chief, Big Nick, and two of the firemen got aboard the Seagrave, and started turning the engine's hand crank. After ten to fifteen minutes, their rigorous cranking produced nothing but a disappointing, **cough!** It seemed the freezing weather was getting to everyone—and *everything*—including the new-fangled fire engine.

Finally, the Seagrave gave an optimistic sputter. On the next crank, it started!

"YIPPEE! WOO HOO!" Amid excited hoots and cheers of joy, the big fire house doors were pushed open! The brand new Seagrave was heading out! The bounty-laden land-barge blew back an impressive, black cloud to announce her maiden departure!

All the eager cheers were suddenly reduced to disappointed, *"Oh, no's . . ."* however, when the Seagrave got bogged down in the heavy snow within several feet of exiting the fire house. It simply could not overcome the huge, icy snowdrifts on the driveway. What the metallic head-turner had in looks—she definitely lacked in guts.

The pitiful machine just could not get enough traction to get going. There was simply too much snow in front of the wheels, and it was far too slippery for the rear wheels to get any traction. All the firemen came out to help push the Seagrave, but it was no use.

With their frozen hands on their hips, the stunned gang just stood there, looking with bewilderment at the sad sight. The beautiful Seagrave, heaping with holiday promise, was hopelessly snow bound.

A familiar *whinny* could be heard from inside the horse stalls. Once a fire horse, always a fire horse—Major knew what needed to be done! And so did Big Nick.

Nick went inside and got Major harnessed up. He then hooked Major to the Seagrave's front bumper with chains and straps. Without much effort at all, Major just walked the helpless machine right out of the massive snow bank!

"YIP, YIP! YA HOO!" The crew went wild with round two of excited cheers!

Nick drove Major, and the chief steered the Seagrave while two firemen rode the tailboard—and off they all went with their holiday bounty to the Markford Orphanage for Christmas!

With his usual sense of purpose, Major cheerfully pulled the brand new—but snow-dead—Seagrave. It was quite a sight to see! The state-of-the-art Seagrave, with its glossy, apple-red paint job and elaborate gold-leaf lettering and designs, looked like a horse-drawn time machine!

The brass bell was ringing, and the firemen in back waved and smiled as they kept a jolly watch over the load of coats and colorful Christmas presents, which were nearly overflowing!

Snow was flying from Major's hooves, and flurries were also falling from the dark, grey sky. Blaze was leaping and bouncing up and down to get through the deep snowdrifts, working hard to keep up with Major without being buried in the white mounds, herself! Luckily, it was a short trip to the orphanage from the fire house.

Dave arrived at the orphanage with Spike, Emmy, and the McConnell's just in time! Major and the Seagrave were almost to the driveway! As Christopher bounded through the snow toward the front door, Dave helped Spike, Emmy, Sarah, and baby Laura from the wagon.

May came out under the portico, greeting Spike, Emmy, Sarah, and baby Laura with hugs and smiles, saying, *"Brrrrr! It's so cold! I'm so glad you all came!"*

Sarah smiled, and Emmy said, "Wouldn' t-a missed it for *nothin'!*" as they hurried inside where the warmth of the holiday was upon them.

As Major turned the Seagrave into the orphanage's driveway, they hit a gigantic, deep, snowdrift with enough speed that it sent up a huge rooster tail of pure, white snow-spray! As they rolled right through the deep snow bank, all the firemen gave Major loud, triumphant, cheers!

"THEY'RE HERE! THEY'RE HERE!" could be heard throughout the orphanage as the children were all peering out of the windows, smiling and waving at the amazing, heart-warming sight of a real Christmas coming right toward them!

As Major, the Seagrave, the firemen, and Blaze all came to a stop at the entry, they were met with squeals of excitement and a collection of cheery grins bright enough to illuminate the grey, snowy sky! Nick about brought the house down when he had Major perform the "Major smile!"

Because it was so cold, Nick and the firemen guided the children into an orderly line so everyone who wanted to had a chance to quickly pat Major. As the wards finished their turn, they headed into the warm, great hall. The children sat, waiting anxiously around the big, glittering tree as the presents were unloaded. While they waited, Sister Barbara Elizabeth played Christmas carols on the piano, and everyone heartily sang along.

Mr. Bloomquist was nowhere in sight.

It was finally time! The Christmas celebration was about to begin! May pulled the wagons full of paper cones near the splendid tree. After all their patient waiting, every single child was individually fitted with a new, warm and wonderful navy blue or brown winter coat! Even Christopher was wearing a new, blue coat!

Then every child received a small, wrapped toy such as a whistle, yo-yo, jacks, a paper doll, lacing card, or spinning top—and for the little ones, rattles and teething rings. And last, each was given a goodie-filled paper cone containing peanuts, candy, cookies, a red-and-white candy cane, and an amazing, bright orange tangerine! It was truly an amazing spectacle!

Yes, for as long as anyone could remember, there had always been a special bond between the Markford Orphanage and the Markford Fire Department . . . especially at Christmas! And today was one of those memory-filled days that makes remembering . . . *something very special.*

May looked around the orphanage. Everywhere she looked, she saw smiling adults bustling about, caring for the needs of the children. She saw gentle patience and thoughtful kindness. She saw joyful service and thankful gratitude. She saw steady guidance, and the efforts of hard work being acknowledged. She saw the kind of atmosphere where children could *thrive*. May Hollyday knew she was exactly where she was supposed to be.

With the heater working, the warm coats came off, and the older children helped the younger ones take their prized, new coats to their sleeping quarters before Cooky's treats and a Christmas buffet was served. As May was watching the joy unfold, two friends in navy blue coats were suddenly standing before her, holding hands and swinging their arms back and forth.

A soft, sweet voice said, "Merry Christmas, May!" May smiled, gently stroking the side of Kathryn's head. She said slowly, "Merry Christmas, Kathryn." As the two friends skipped away, giggling and chatting as they carried their paper cones, May's heart swelled and flowed over with happiness until she felt it in her eyes.

As May watched Kathryn and her new friend head upstairs together to put their coats away, she smiled warmly as she heard her momma's voice echoing in her head: *"Child . . . you look from the inside, and see what you see . . . ."*

As May bent her head to wipe the liquid happiness from her eye, she noticed one, last paper cone left in the wooden wagon, and she picked it up. She looked down into her pocket, making sure the handkerchief she had made for Nick was still there. Patting it with confident assurance, she nodded, then she disappeared.

Responding to the three knocks, Mr. Bloomquist stiffly turned from his chair, scowling as he looked at his door. Grunting and panting, he worked very hard to get to the edge of his seat, and grimaced as he leaned heavily on his walking stick just to be able to stand. Mr. Bloomquist was in excruciating pain.

Hobbling now, with an exaggerated limp matched only by his deep and heavy frown, he labored to make it to the door. Holding the wall, he steadied himself, straightening the perfect posture he wanted the world to see. He opened his door just a crack and peeked outside. No one was there.

Grumbling about the inconvenience, he used his stick as a cane, and shuffled his feet into position. He opened his door wider to further investigate. Scowling, he looked left. Then right. His cranky grimace softened as he looked down at his doorknob.

He steadied his balance again, and carefully lifted the treat-filled paper cone hanging from his black porcelain doorknob.

As he drew it closer to his eyes and peered inside, his deeply chiseled scowl began to fade away. Tucked in with the peanuts, the tangerine, the candies, the cookies, and the candy cane . . . was an exquisitely embroidered handkerchief, decorated with green, satin-stitch holly leaves, and perfectly round, nubby, holly berries made from red French knots.

As he touched the tiny, perfect stitches, he whispered softly—to no one, *"Isn't it beautiful?"*

Then, very slowly—he tenderly whispered, *"Extravagantly . . . beautiful . . . ."*

Mr. Bloomquist was bent and buckled to the breaking point as he lifted the handkerchief, revealing the sentiment sewn on the opposite corner. Stitched in red embroidery floss were the words, *"With love, at Christmas."*

In the dining hall, Cooky, Mr. Paul, and Father Sammon brought out tray after tray of Cooky's beautiful, delicious baked goods, with Father Sammon "sampling" a cinnamon roll as he set down his tray! The staff brought out enough potatoes and gravy to feed a crowd, along with the platters of sliced turkey and ham the ladies sent from the firehouse.

As everyone made their way through the buffet line, Nick went outside to check on Blaze and Major. It was still very chilly and snowing. As the crowd enjoyed warm mounds of potatoes and savory slices of turkey and ham—all covered with delicious gravy, there stood Major in the freezing cold, proud and dutiful. Devoted Blaze was firmly seated in the snow next to him.

Big Nick looked down at his shoes, and then back at the two of them, standing guard together. They seemed cold. And lonesome. Nick thought of his amazing Major, and how all of the joy of this day would not have been possible without his mighty effort. Major had actually helped the nameless, lifeless machine that would soon replace him.

Nick stood outside for a long time, talking to Major, and brushing off the cold snow. The lunch buffet had finished, and as soon as the after-lunch music and singing had ended, the Christmas celebration would be over.

It was then that Big Nick had his bright idea! He quickly swished the snow off his own head, and reached into the big, inside chest pocket of his coat. He unrolled the hat May had made for him, and as he pulled it on, he was already smiling!

He unhooked Major, and carefully walked him under the covered portico. Nick paused to eyeball the size of the doorway. Then he began eyeballing the size of the evergreen wreath with the red velvet bow. He *wondered if . . . .*

Nick lifted the huge wreath off of the dark, front door. As Major stood ready, Big Nick put the colossal wreath right over Major's massive head, settling it down with a perfect fit like a festive, evergreen Christmas collar with a red bow tie!

Nick laughed out loud, as Major actually seemed pleased to be wearing it! He had Major lower his head to fit through the door opening, and Nick slowly walked Major and Blaze through the huge doorway.

The great hall was filled to capacity with the heartwarming glow of the Christmas spirit! To the happy cheers from all in the room, Nick, Blaze, and Major made their way into the great hall. Major's rhythmic forward motion had his big hooves clopping slowly on the wooden floor, and sent the bells sewn onto the red, velvet ribbon dancing and jingling!

Big Nick directed in a soothing, low tone, *"Hold, Major."* And, like a picture-postcard, Major stood by the glorious spruce tree, wearing the big, beautiful, evergreen and holly Christmas wreath. He was surrounded by warm, happy, grateful children. Without a doubt, Major had helped make their wish for a warm Christmas come true. Major had truly saved Christmas! As everyone in the room applauded Major with wild claps of appreciation, Nick had Major bow!

Dave and Sister Barbara Elizabeth ended the celebration with a song. As Dave played the guitar, Sister Barbara Elizabeth asked everyone to join in singing, *"Silent Night."*

In a most special celebration, the heart of one, amazing fire horse was recognized, and everyone in the room knew they would never forget this day.

Nick and May stood side-by-side—his big arm draped around her shoulder, and her hand reaching up to hold his. As he gazed around the great hall, Nick was almost overwhelmed by a flood of warmth and *new* memories. And as he watched May, carrying all the promise of his own family . . . Nick had never felt more settled or sure, and he *loved* that feeling.

Together, Nick and May looked at magnificent Major standing next to them— obedient, loyal, capable, and proud. As Blaze nuzzled in next to them, Nick and

May smiled wide at one another as they sang *"Silent Night,"* their joyful voices joining in and melding with all the others in the room to create the sound of a choir.

That day, Major had earned the name May gave him the first moment she saw him.

Major had truly become, ***"CHRISTMAS MAJOR!"***

About the Authors

"Christmas Major" is both written and illustrated by Dave Hubert, who devoted thirty years to the firefighting profession, serving in many different positions including firefighter, fire training officer, and fire defense coordinator, prior to his retirement in 1997 as Fire Captain from Orange County Fire Authority in Southern California. Barbara didn't want to be shown as an author, but Dave insisted, because they do everything as a team.

Dave and Barbara Hubert with Blaze in 2011.

Throughout his fire service career, Dave has also produced a wide variety of artwork that typically has revolved around the profession he loves and respects so much: the fire service. From his published *"HUBIE"* cartoon series to decorating fire station walls, retirement tributes, and attention-getting humorous cartoons in fire training books, Dave's illustrations abound.

Soon after retiring, Dave used his remarkable artistic vision and ability to complete the restoration of a 1902 horse-drawn steam fire engine. For over sixteen years now, his "Steamer Team" of retired firefighters has donated their time by participating in statewide community and charity events, representing the California State Firefighters' Association (CSFA) in the interest of public safety and fire prevention education.

Recently refocusing his creative talent in yet another direction, Dave has written this fictional story because he wanted to highlight the significant role that fire horses played throughout the early fire service with its horse-drawn equipment.

Dave and Barbara have two children and five grandchildren. Their son, Mark, is a firefighter paramedic for Orange County Fire Authority and their daughter, Michelle, teaches elementary school locally.

Steamer during Lone Pine Film Festival Parade, 2005. Horse team driven by George Liblin of G&F Carriages with Blaze riding in seat.

Products from Hubie Pictures

HUBIE and the Fire Service

HUBIE and the Fire Service is a humorous cartoon book that looks inside the Fire Service profession by a real insider . . . Dave *"HUBIE"* Hubert, a thirty-year artist and Firefighter.

Rich with color and packed with HUBIE cartoon humor, this high-quality, Collector's Edition cartoon book covers the highs and lows of life as a firefighter. With over 350 cartoons of lighthearted fun and jokes, this first of its kind edition is true to the Fire Service profession. It illustrates life at the fireground, in the fire house, and employs firefighter humor to help ease the sadness of frequent exposure to tragedies. Also covered in this book are excerpts from the story of Dave's restoration of the 1902 Steam Fire Engine featured in the new DVD, *THE STEAMER-AN AMERICAN ICON.*

Presented in a colorful collector's slip case, this beautiful 9 x 12, hardcover has a gold-embossed red cover, gilt-edged pages, and over 300 high-quality, color pages of original artwork and HUBIE cartoons from the *CALIFORNIA FIRE SERVICE MAGAZINE* and other Fire Service publications. Available at a special introductory discount, this $75.00 book makes the perfect gift!

Exclusive Collector's Edition 40% Introductory Offer $~~75.00~~ $45.00, plus sales tax and shipping.

The Steamer, an American Icon

AMERICA, 1902. As mighty white horses came thundering down the street, excitement, color, and sound greeted those who stopped in their tracks to watch the steam fire engine racing to a fire—bells clanging, whistles blowing, and smoke billowing from this majestic historical classic.

This colorful documentary is about the discovery, restoration, and resurrection of a 1902 American Steam Fire Engine. In 1991, recessed in the shadows of an old barn in Fallbrook, California, one of these pioneer fire engines was found. The journey that followed is inspirational and amazing. From some of the most unlikely sources, piece by piece, this American Icon was brought back to life.

Whether it's learning about rich firefighting history, listening to team anecdotes, watching the steamer pump water, or enjoying Blaze the fire dog and powerful horse teams, this DVD is bound to keep your interest!

Known as *"The American,"* this fire engine is an American treasure. From its glorious origins as Engine No. 1 in Reno, Nevada in 1902 to its remarkable resurrection, this fascinating, true story is captivating from start to finish!

Today, **THE STEAMER** represents the best of us . . . the best of America.

Pre-publication Offer $~~29.99~~ $19.99, plus sales tax and shipping.

Christmas Major
The Fire Horse Who Saved Christmas

This heartwarming story tells about an abandoned orphan and a spirited draft horse coming together to save lives and care for others. Readers will learn about the exciting world of fire horses, and travel back in time to the early 1900s when these mighty animals were so dedicated and loyal that they would obediently pull huge fire wagons straight towards their greatest fear—the perilous ravages of fire! Learn how a young colt destined for life as a plow horse, through a twist of fate, becomes one of these incredible heroes!

CHRISTMAS MAJOR is much more than a Christmas story. It's an adventure about character, loyalty, love, firefighting, and the magical bond between humans and animals.

$18.95, plus sales tax and shipping.

Order at **www.hubiepictures.com**